HENRI DUNANT: *MAN IN WHITE*

BY RUDOLPH M. STOIBER

HENRI DUNANT: MAN IN WHITE

ABELARD-SCHUMAN

London New York Toronto

LONDON	NEW YORK	TORONTO
Abelard-Schuman	Abelard-Schuman	Abelard-Schuman
Limited	Limited	Canada Limited
8 King St. WC2	6 West 57th St.	896 Queen St. W.

Printed in the United States of America

CONTENTS

CHAPTER ONE

1828

May was cold and rainy that year. Up in the Swiss mountains it snowed, not only high on Mont Blanc and the St. Bernard Pass, but down on the slopes as far as the first peasant huts. In the valley below, it rained. For weeks, the fog had not lifted from the lake; and when the rain did stop for a while, dripping blankets of cloud hid the mountains.

Suddenly, one morning, there was silence. The gurgling in the drains on the roofs stopped; so did the splashing in the gutters. Only single drops, in lengthening intervals, splashed onto the pavements from the roofs and branches. After the days of rushing rain, it was so quiet that single drops could be heard as they fell.

Then the wind began. It came howling out of the valley of the Rhone just as the children left for school, so that they had to clutch their hats and hold their feet firmly on the ground. The bold, warm wind pulled at the foliage of the trees, but the leaves were still too small and tightly curled to be pulled from the branches. The wind wiped patches of snow from the mountains; it sucked up puddles in the vineyard; it lifted veils of fog from the lake and touseled the clouds until they were rings of white hair around the heads of the mountains.

At noon, when the children came home for lunch, the wind was still blowing. It pushed their backs as they ran home, allowing them no chance to dawdle. Only when the youngest children began to yawn and rub their eyes that evening did the wind tire, too, and settle down. By then, the sky was swept clean and the setting sun poured rosy light over the land.

At dusk, when the shops were closing and the clerks were sweeping dust from the stores into the street, the people of Geneva threw open their windows, leaned out, and said: "It's getting warmer. Maybe spring is coming after all!"

However, the windows of the house at 286 Rue Verdaine were not opened; and there, nobody looked out. In an oak-panelled room with closed windows and drawn curtains, the master of the house, Monsieur Dunant, restlessly paced the floor.

"No, no! I cannot believe that, Doctor! I refuse to accept it! That thought is absolutely against my firmest convictions!" Monsieur Dunant addressed a delicate, grey-haired man who sat in a leather armchair near the fire. Doctor Molard opened the instrument bag in his lap, checked its contents, closed the bag again, and raised his head.

"Why?"

"Man has become rational!" The dark young man, his pale face framed by a well-trimmed beard, resumed his pacing. "Man has become rational, my dear doctor," he lectured, "rational! Wars are possible only where there are borders," he went on. "But people have already begun to conquer the borders with their minds — to break down the arbitrary barriers which separate them. Some day, men will realize that they are brothers..."

"I don't know," said the doctor. "Only yesterday I came across a case..."

"But, my dear sir, you cannot take a single case from your practice and draw from it conclusions on the condition of all mankind!"

"I don't know."

"People who know each other cannot shoot each other!" Chin up and hands behind his back, the young man walked back and forth between the table and the window.

With an awkward gesture, the doctor set down his bag, then said: "Yes, but do people know each other? Do parents know their children; husbands, their wives? Do people really know each other?"

"They will learn to know each other! The exchange of newspapers will make available information about foreign countries, and increased familiarity will bring people together. I heard recently of a remarkable experiment in that direction. Scientists now look forward to the instantaneous sending of messages over great distances by means of electricity and magnetism. Who knows when the time will come when we can transmit a message, swift as lightning, from one capital to another? The monarchs will be the first to use such an invention, and the Emperor of Austria will have an answer within hours from the Tsar or the King of Prussia. Are wars still possible when people are so close?"

"Physical distance will shrink; that is true."

"Steamships can cross the ocean in less than four weeks right now. You know yourself, Doctor, that in England a certain Stephenson has built a steam engine with cars which will be able to carry men and goods from one place to another, without human or animal power, using only the steam from heated water! Progress can no longer be halted, and progress will make war impossible."

"May God grant that you are right," said the doctor. He rose from his chair and walked slowly over to the window. Drawing back the curtains, he looked up at the sky. "It has cleared. We could open the windows now." He pushed back the bolt, Monsieur Dunant stepped to his side, and together they opened the inner frames of the double windows.

Just then, the door to the adjoining room was opened.

Between the green velvet draperies appeared a stout, elderly woman. She walked carefully, carrying a pewter basin filled with water. Both men turned around, looked at her eagerly, and were disappointed when she shook her head. As the old woman reached the other side of the room, she noticed that the doctor was about to open the outer windows.

"For Heaven's sake!" she screamed. Holding the basin in her outstretched hands, she begged, "No draft, Doctor! Please, I beg of you, no draft!"

Doctor Molard shrugged, smiled vaguely, and pushed the windows closed again. The nurse looked at him reproachfully, shook her head, and left the room.

"See, there is your progress," said the doctor. He dropped back into the leather cushions of the armchair. "We teach today in our medical schools that fresh air and exposure to the sun are good for every patient. But I am not allowed to open the window, not even in a room outside the sickroom, because the nurse does not permit it. The stupidity and superstition of the masses hold back the few who have adopted progressive ideas."

"Not in my house!" answered the young man. Stepping over to the window, he drew aside the curtains and unhooked the bolt once more. Just when he was about to open the window again, the nurse returned, carrying her basin newly filled with boiling water. In spite of the steam which rose in front of her face, she noticed the window.

"Do you want Madame to die?" she asked. "Instead of being helpful, you are doing the worst possible thing!"

The nurse put the basin down on a table, wiped her hands on her white apron, and pushed Monsieur Dunant aside. She closed and locked the windows and pulled together the heavy curtains. Having picked up her steaming basin, she paused in front of the doctor as if to give him further directions. But Doctor Molard motioned her on, saying:

"Go on in to Madame, Marie. Monsieur and I will not try to do anything else that we consider sensible. And call me when it is time."

"Do you see what will happen to your progressive ideas?" continued the doctor, when the nurse had disappeared behind the green draperies. "A few minds are ready to receive the fresh air of the new ideas — ideas of brotherhood, of one family of man. But the masses keep their windows closed, refusing the fresh breeze. 'There have always been wars, therefore there will always be wars!' That is their opinion; that is the stale air in which they were raised. These people will be right as long as they are in the majority, and I am afraid that will always be the case."

"That is just what I refuse to believe! We are at the beginning of a new era of development, at the beginning of that nineteenth century which will someday be called the 'Great!' Just wait, Doctor! Today we are only a few, we who are dedicated to progress, but tomorrow . . ."

Now the doctor was stirred to excitement. "Tomorrow, today's handful of sincerely progressive men will be dead. Their numbers will not have increased by a single one."

"Their numbers are growing every day." The young man's eyes were shining. "Man's life span is lengthening;

you must know that yourself, Doctor. The death rate of children is dropping, and the population grows every year. Since 1805, the population of Europe alone has increased from one hundred and seventy five to two hundred and twenty million."

The doctor wished to answer that mere figures proved nothing, but he was interrupted.

"Doctor!"

"Yes, I am coming." He picked up his bag and pushed his way quickly through the green draperies into the adjoining room.

Monsieur Dunant, left behind, stood uncertainly at the closed door. The room was perfectly silent. He turned around and left the salon. In the corridor, his voice rang out:

"Papa, David! Hello, Papa!"

When Dunant returned to the room, he realized suddenly that it was indeed stuffy and smelled stale. The fire burned a glassy red, almost without a flame. Perspiration rose on his forehead. He felt stifled, surrounded by heat and the threatening stillness. He rushed to a window and opened it, grateful for the balmy breeze which carried into the room the scent of moist leaves, earth and spring.

"Is it time?"

Madame's father, Henri Colladon, entered the room, followed by David Dunant, elder brother of the young man.

"Yes, Papa, I think it is. The doctor has been inside for a while."

"Shouldn't you close the window?"

"It's so terribly hot in here."

"We'll be able to stand that, Son. We'll keep the door to the corridor open."

"It isn't only the heat, it's . . . ."

"Why don't we sit down?" said David, choosing the leather armchair for himself.

The other two were too excited to remain seated.

"Jean, please do close the window. I am sure it isn't good to have it wide open." The white-haired gentleman walked over to the fireplace. "I can feel a cold draft." When the young man hesitated, he continued: "Please! I can feel the cold evening breeze in my old bones."

So Monsieur Dunant closed the window for the third time, and pulled the curtains together once more.

"How long has he been in there?" asked Monsieur David.

Jean Dunant looked up to the black pendulum clock between the two windows. It was almost eight-thirty. "More than twenty minutes," he said.

Just then a suppressed cry was heard from the other room.

"That was Anne," whispered the old man.

Monsieur Dunant was silent. He leaned against the table, waiting for another sound to break the silence of the room. The clock did so first. It started to rattle; it groaned and creaked inside before it began to strike the notes that sounded the half-hour.

At the last stroke of the clock, the men heard the doorknob of the adjoining room turning. Doctor Molard pushed his way through the draperies. He had taken off his coat, and the sleeves of his white shirt were pushed up to his elbows. He seemed satisfied and gay. It was not the shy, delicate scientist of the early evening who came into the room, but a confident and resolute worker. He walked up to Monsieur Dunant and shook his hand.

"My best wishes, Monsieur," he said. "Now Europe has two hundred and twenty million and one inhabitants."

"One male?"

"Yes, you have a son."

Now Dunant grasped both of the doctor's hands, stammering, "Thank you, Doctor."

But Doctor Molard refused the thanks. "It wasn't I who made the choice. By the way," he added, "you can go in now."

The young man stepped back to allow his father-in-law to enter the room, but the older man pushed him ahead. "You must go first, Jean. You are the important man today."

As the three men, accompanied by the doctor, entered the adjoining room, Madame Dunant raised her head from the lace-covered pillow. Her husband went to the bedside and bent over his wife's hand. "I thank you, Anne," he said, looking down with a shy and helpless smile. "I'll certainly bring you some flowers later on; sorry I didn't think of them before. Forgive me . . ."

Madame Dunant stroked back the black hair which fell boyishly over his forehead.

"Well, don't you want to have a look at your firstborn?"

asked the new grandfather. He and David were bending over the cradle which stood near the bed.

"Go on, look at him," said his wife. "I wonder if you will like him."

The nurse took the newborn child from the cradle and held him up to his father. Dunant did not know how to receive him and held out his hands awkwardly.

"This way, Monsieur," said the nurse, showing him how to bend his arms.

"He weighs so little," said the father, as he smiled at the tiny red face which peeked out of a bundle of lace and pillows.

"That's nice!" said Doctor Molard. "Not satisfied!"

"I am well satisfied," said Monsieur Dunant, bending over the infant. "I am well satisfied with you, Jean Henri. Do you hear me, Jean Henri?"

"He doesn't know that is his name," said the grandfather.

"His mother and I decided on that name long ago."

"It would have been too bad if the good Jean Henri had turned out to be a girl!" They all laughed at Monsieur Colladon's joke.

"You are Jean Henri Dunant," the young man said to the child. "Born in Geneva, Switzerland, May 8th, 1828."

"Son of an honest citizen of the splendid city of Geneva," Monsieur Colladon added. "Yes, and do not forget, your father is a member of the municipal council."

"And your grandfather is the mayor of Avully," said Dunant.

"And this gentleman," said the grandfather, drawing David Dunant closer, "This gentleman with the sinister face is your Uncle David, a prosperous publisher and bookseller, whose heir you will someday be if your uncle doesn't make up his mind to get married."

"Now that he knows our professions and titles," said Monsieur David, "we should ask him what he wants to be."

"A banker, of course," said his father.

"I think he looks suited to a diplomatic career — ambasssador, politician, or something like that," stated the grandfather.

"I am for a business career," said the child's uncle.

"And what does the mother say?" asked Doctor Molard.

"Let him do whatever he wants to do, whatever he wants to do with his whole heart."

At that moment the corners of the tiny mouth began to quiver, the little nose wrinkled, and baby Jean Henri let out his first wails.

"Why does he cry, when we are just showing him his promising future?" asked his father.

"Babies have to cry," said the nurse, who was busy putting a cold compress on Madame's forehead. When she had finished, she took the baby from Monsieur and put him back into the cradle.

"Perhaps he is crying because you cannot spare him the common fate of all mankind, despite your good fortune as a family." Doctor Molard had put on his coat again and was replacing the instruments in his bag. "Envy and jealousy, hostility and loneliness, war, illness and death. Who is spared?"

"Hush, hush!" The nurse was upset by the doctor's gloomy predictions. She began rocking the cradle as if she could shake the dreary words away from the little boy. "How can you say such things in front of a child?" she asked. Then she began to sing to the wailing baby, "Seven angels standing by my baby; two by his little feet, two by his little hands..."

The four men said goodbye. Doctor Molard promised to visit the next morning, and left with the others. As they closed the door, they could still hear the nurse's voice, "...golden treasures will they bring my baby, ripe old age and health, luck and wisdom for my baby... for my baby...."

As the men crossed the room where they had waited for the child to be born, Dunant exclaimed to his friend: "Just the same, Doctor! There will come a time when war will cease!"

Doctor Molard only shrugged his shoulders.

CHAPTER TWO

1835

A children's party was held on Henri's seventh birthday at "La Monaie," the Dunants' mansion in one of the suburbs of Geneva. They had left Grandfather Colladon's home shortly after Henri's birth. The garden of the country house certainly was the right place for parties and games. The weather was pleasant, too, with warm sunshine, blue skies and small white clouds.

The little guests were treated to hot chocolate and cake at low white tables out of doors. They seemed to be enjoying it, and this was not surprising, for Madame Dunant had not invited the children of prominent families of Gen-

eva, but orphans who did not go to many parties. Monsieur
Dunant was the orphans' guardian and Miss Mathilde, of
the orphanage, had brought the children to Henri's birthday party.

As soon as the dishes had been removed and the little
guests given permission to put the leftover cookies into
their pockets, they swarmed out into the various parts of
the garden. They played hide and seek and blind man's
buff behind the shrubs, and a group of girls was swinging
underneath the elm trees. Those who had to wait for their
turn could be heard singing: "Frère Jacques, Frère Jacques, dormez vous, dormez vous . . . " and every time they
came to the last line, "bim, bam, boom," they ran over to
the swings and gave them another push, laughing with mer-
riment.

Madame Dunant and Miss Mathilde were standing on
top of the staircase which led into the garden, watching the
gaiety. They could not see everything that was going on
because the tall trees bordering the small paths obstruct-
ed the view. They could see a little red dress here, hear a
burst of laughter there, but the next second they would be
gone, hidden by the flowers and shrubs of the large garden.

"You are very kind, Madame," Miss Mathilde said, and
the white wings on her hat danced up and down as she
emphasized her statement by nodding her head. "You are
so kind to these poor children."

"Oh, it is our duty, Miss Mathilde," Madame Dunant
answered, "that we, who are blessed with moderate wealth,
help the poor. And who could be poorer than an orphan?"

"Yes," Miss Mathilde sighed with pity, and the end of her nose seemed to grow to a sharper point. "Will you get off the lawn," she suddenly cried, shaking her long white forefinger towards a girl who was running after a ball which had jumped away from her. Then she took up the interrupted conversation once more. "You said it was your duty, as if the carrying out of this duty was a simple matter. But how many other people . . ."

"I am happy, if the children feel happy," Madame Dunant interrupted.

"You may be sure of that," Miss Mathilde said. "What are you doing over there?" she asked in a shrill voice, noticing a little fellow in between the laurel bushes. Then she continued in the same sweet, singing voice as before: "The children look forward to these hours all year long — Emile, keep your hands off the lilac blossoms. You are only supposed to smell them!"

"Please don't scold the children. They don't do any harm."

But Miss Mathilde was a strict mistress to those entrusted to her care. "Pardon me, Madame Dunant, where would we be if everyone was allowed to do what he pleased? You would soon have no roses left on the bushes. The beautiful lawn would be stamped down, the flowers would be torn off and thrown away, and all that damage would be done stupidly and carelessly, for children have no regard for beauty."

"That I don't believe," Madame Dunant said emphatically. "You must pardon me, I am sure you have more experience than I have, but I cannot believe children care nothing for beauty. I have seen Henri standing in front of a flower for hours, just admiring it. And after he has walked away and I have thought he was tired of it, then he has come back, again losing himself in its beauty. I believe that children, too, can appreciate beauty."

Miss Mathilde raised her head a little bit and smiled. "Don't forget, Madame, that your Henri is a quite different, extraordinary child. You can't compare him with uneducated orphans."

"I don't think he is any different from the rest of the children," the mother said, lowering her eyes.

"Oh, I tell you, he is different. He only acts like other children. It is a sign of a great soul that he associates with them, as if no differences of rank existed between him and those paupers." And sighing in admiration, she closed her speech saying, "I always tell Miss Hélène, Henri Dunant is a little man with a big soul."

"Oh, Miss Mathilde, you shouldn't say that," Madame Dunant said with an embarrassed smile, "I might become too proud of him." And looking around she asked: "Where is my 'big soul,' anyway?"

Miss Mathilde was also looking around and the white wings of her hat began to wiggle like big ears. "I just saw his curly head. I think Henri had his eyes blindfolded, so he must be the blind man's buff, if I may call the little gentleman that. I hope he didn't get lost, blindfolded."

"Henri!"

No answer. Madame Dunant called Henri again. Again

no answer. Nothing could be heard but the shouting and laughing of the children everywhere in the garden. The girls were still singing "Frère Jacques" and laughing gaily when they came to the last line.

"Do you want me to call him also?" Miss Mathilde asked, clearing her throat in advance.

"No, thank you. Don't bother. He knows my voice — Henri!"

Finally the answer came, a happy sounding "Yes," and Henri came forward from behind one of the trees. He was trying to untie the knot in the scarf tied over his eyes, but he couldn't do it. So pulling it off his forehead, and waving it in his hand, he came running down the path. "Hello, Mama. I am having so much fun today."

Miss Mathilde, seeing the boy, looked extremely shocked. "See what he looks like," escaped from her lips, but she wished she could take back the words. Madame Dunant did not show her own surprise. "I suppose it is only a joke," she said to herself, looking at her son. Henri seemed to grow uncomfortable under his mother's strict look. He reached into his coat pocket, trying to find a handkerchief. Finding none, however, he took the scarf he had been using to play blind-man's buff and wiped his forehead with it.

"I am afraid you will not find a handkerchief in this coat," his mother said sternly. Miss Mathilde began eagerly to explain to Madame Dunant: "No, because our boys are supposed to have their handkerchiefs in the right-hand pocket of their trousers, according to the rules of our institution. The girls, on the other hand . . ."

Madame Dunant did not pay any attention. "What does this mean?" she asked Henri, as he finally stood before her.

The boy was perspiring, his matted brown hair hanging into his face and his white stockings showing grass stains. He swallowed several times and said, "We have been playing blind man's buff, and I fell down."

"I don't mean that," his mother said, "you have other stockings. I mean the coat."

Henri was wearing a mended, dirty grey coat of cheap material with his own velvet pants.

"That coat?" Henri asked.

"Yes, where did you get that coat?"

"I gave my coat to Kurtli and put on his instead."

The two women became a little embarrassed by the answer, given in such a natural, matter-of-fact manner, as if he didn't feel the slightest regret about having traded his brown velvet coat for the shabby coat of an orphan.

Miss Mathilde, who was accustomed to speaking to children, was the first one to find her voice. In a gentle, reproachful manner she said: "You should not have done that, little man. Didn't you notice how dirty the coat was? I am sure yours was a much prettier one."

"He only got it today, from his grandfather," his mother put in.

"Now you see," Miss Mathilde confirmed.

"But Mama," Henri said in surprise, looking straight into his mother's eyes, "you yourself read to me only yesterday that Our Lord Jesus said, what you do unto the least of my brothers, you have done unto me. Have you forgotten it already?" And, as his mother did not answer, he asked again: "Don't you remember?"

"That's right, son, but . . ."

"That's why I gave Kurtli my coat."

"Because Our Lord Jesus said so?" Miss Mathilde looked at him with an astonished look in her eyes.

"And also because we became friends while we played."

"And I suppose he took the coat gladly, your new friend?" Miss Mathilde asked, her mouth drawn to a narrow line.

"No, he did not want to, at first," Henri said. "He said that he would feel funny with such a pretty coat among the other boys. But I told him to go ahead and take it. I had not felt funny with it and I would not mind wearing his at all. He took it then."

Madame Dunant took her son's hand and led him towards the house. Miss Mathilde, following them, said she would see that Kurtli did not get the coat soiled and that he gave it back properly.

"No!" Henri cried and began to kick and pull at his mother's hand. "I gave it to Kurtli and I don't want it back!"

"Don't worry, Miss Mathilde," Madame Dunant said, pushing her boy through the glass door, "we have no right to stop Henri if he wants to give his coat away." Mother and son crossed the hall, climbed the wide staircase covered with red carpets and walked up to the second floor.

After reaching the first landing, Henri pulled loose and put his hand into his pocket. "Look, mother, all these things I found in Kurtli's coat pockets. And I can keep them all,

because he can keep everything in my pockets, the handkerchief with my initials on it and the beautiful pocket
knife I got from Uncle David." But his mother did not
stop. He had to run after her to catch up with her in front
of the little chest with the mirror. "Please look," he repeated, spreading his precious things out on top of it: a piece
of cord, one, two, three — five acorns, one nail, one dead
earthworm . . .

Henri did not feel any too comfortable when he saw the
dead worm on the marble top of the chest, and it definitely
was too much for his mother. "Oh! No!" she cried, "take
that fellow's dirty rag off at once!" When Henri, who had
never before seen his mother so excited, hesitated, she repeated angrily, "Don't you hear me? Take that coat off!"

"Yes, Mother."

"Louis," she called to a servant who was just coming
down the corridor, "Louis, will you please throw this rag
and that trash on the chest into the garbage, or better still,
burn it all." Looking at Henri she pointed to the floor without saying a word. Henri took off Kurtli's coat slowly,
folded it up as he was used to folding up his own clothes
at night, and put it down carefully, almost tenderly, on the
red carpet. When he started to put his friend's possessions
down, too, his mother stopped him, crying, "Don't you
touch those things again. Louis will take care of them."

When Madame Dunant saw how deeply disturbed Henri looked after the incident, she patted his head, saying,
"There is a great deal you have to learn, Henri. First of

all, that there is a limit to everything, even to generosity. My big soul!" Bending down, she kissed his forehead. "So, go up to your room now, wash up, and put on your grey coat. It is almost dinner time. Mama is going to change her dress, too." Henri did not move from the spot, so his mother whispered into his ear, "We will see what kind of a surprise we have waiting for our Henri at the dinner table."

Henri did not answer.

"Don't you want to know?"

Henri shook his head.

"Not curious at all?"

"I know anyway," Henri said, "a cake with seven candles on it. Last year the cake had six candles and next year it will have eight."

"Perhaps so, we will see. Run along now. If you promise to get clean and neat by yourself, I won't send Marie up to your room. You can get ready alone, like a young man."

Henri nodded and walked on to his room stiffly, thinking: I would have loved to keep that nail; it was such a nice one. Maybe Louis will give it back to me if I ask him for it. I could have used it. It had such a sharp point. I'll ask Louis if I may have it.

There was indeed a big chocolate cake in the middle of the birthday table, with seven small white candles on it. Next to it was a crystal vase filled with delicate green twigs and the first roses of the year — seven red roses.

It was getting dark outside and the candles in the heavy silver candlesticks were lit. Papa Dunant picked up one of them and held its light against the first birthday candle. After he lit it, he said, "This is for Henri, that he may be a happy man, one day." Then he handed the candle in the silver candlestick to his son. Henri rose and lit with it the remaining small candles. "For Papa," he said, when the second candle was burning, "for Mama," as the third one caught the flame. Then he stopped, looking around.

"Well, whose turn is it next?" his mother asked with a smile. The three younger Dunant children looked at their big brother.

"Daniel," Henri said, lighting the fourth candle. Little Daniel smiled proudly and Henri continued, "And this one for my little sister Marie, and this one for Sophie."

"I am the last one," Sophie fretted.

"No, you are not the last one," their mother said, "only six candles are lit so far!"

"And who gets the seventh candle?" Papa Dunant asked.

Henri did not look at anyone. He was looking at the six little flames, swaying in the draft.

"Well?"

Henri, watching the lights glow on the cake, stared at the last candle.

"Henri, you have to light one more," his father reminded him. But the mother silenced him, saying, "Leave him alone, Henri will know whom the seventh candle is for."

That woke Henri from his daydreams, and bending over

the cake, he lit the seventh birthday candle. But the wick did not want to catch the flame, and the wax of the big candle dripped on the chocolate icing. Finally the seventh candle was also burning, a little light with a calm, bluish flame.

"For Kurtli," Henri said softly, "that he too may be a happy man, one day."

1849

"Why don't you want to put any candles on Henri's birth-day cake this year?" Madame Dunant asked her husband, who was watching her set the birthday table from his cosy chair. "I have become so accustomed to seeing one more candle every year."

"There has to be a stop to it sometime, otherwise you will have to light thirty or forty candles some day! It wouldn't be possible to fit that many candles on a cake, or you would have to order the cake at the candlemaker's."

"My goodness, Jean, you are so strange, so easily annoyed lately. You never used to be that way before."

Monsieur Dunant tried hard to make up for his impatience, saying, "You can put the candles on the cake one more year, if you want to. But I think Henri is really too old for it."

"Oh, Jean, he is only a child."

Monsieur Dunant wanted to answer that a boy twenty-one years old was no longer a child; that he no longer had the right to be one. On the contrary, he thought today would be a good day to tell his wife and oldest son that he had decided to let Henri start as an apprentice at the bank of Lullin & Sautter. The maid, who just then entered with a bouquet of fresh roses, stopped him.

The girl was young and her hair was blond. Those two features most distinguished her from the old Marie who had died a year ago. She was still so new to the Dunants that she had not as yet become familiar with the habits of the household, habits that had grown into tradition. She would still put the salt shaker close to Monsieur Dunant's plate, although he never used salt. She didn't know that the children were not supposed to get any water with their meals and she did not know how the birthday table was to be set for the young master, year after year.

That was the reason she asked: "Where shall I put the roses please, Madame?" Every question she had to ask embarrassed her.

But Madame Dunant was very kind and never lost patience, for she kept in mind that the girl was very young indeed and that she might well be serving Henri throughout his lifetime. "They go right here," Madame Dunant said graciously, taking the roses from the new Marie. She reached for a beautifully cut crystal vase which was kept in the corner china closet, and busied herself arranging the half open rosebuds loosely in it. "The roses always go into this crystal vase, loosely, so that their beauty is emphasized."

Spring had entered the room with the roses. It was not a wild spring with rushing warm winds, snow drifts, avalanches and the crackle of popping buds. This year spring was gentle with quiet evenings, a springtime that brought back memories.

"This year we have roses again for Henri's birthday," Madame Dunant said. "We didn't have any last year, it was too cold."

"Yes, it is not always the same. Some years it has been rather cool during May. May can be as warm as a summer month, warm enough to bring in the hay, or it can be a month with snow." Monsieur Dunant noticed that Marie did not quite believe what he said and added, "Yes, it's possible. Do you remember, darling, the year Henri was born? We had snow, and not only high up in the mountains, no, it snowed all the way down the valley. We had snow in Geneva that May 8th, 1828."

Marie left the dining room and went back to the kitchen. After the two were alone again, Monsieur Dunant asked his wife, who was still putting the final touches to the table, "Do you remember, dear?"

"Yes, I do remember," Madame Dunant said, looking

over towards her husband with a strange smile. "That year there were no roses either."

"Of course there were no roses outdoors, but there were some in the hothouse that belonged to Papa Colladon. I remember very well, François got me the roses I gave you from the hothouse."

"François was not with us yet. We had Louis then."

"That does not matter. Somebody brought the roses from the hothouse, and I took the roses to you. It was a big bouquet of red roses. I remember very well, you said . . ."

Seeing a mischievous smile on his wife's face, he became somewhat uncertain.

Madame Dunant was now standing in front of him. Shaking her head a little, her lips were saying "no," very softly.

"Is that true?"

Madame Dunant, bending down to her husband and brushing her hand gently over his coat, removed a piece of thread and said, "You do look very well tonight."

Her husband, stretching himself up to her, kissed her forehead and, as if his question was in regard to last night's omission, he repeated it, greatly concerned: "Is it true that I did not bring you any roses, that time?"

"No, you even said you forgot. But I think it must have been Dr. Molard's fault. I remember you had just had some kind of argument, something in regard to future wars." Settling comfortably on the arm rest of his easy chair, she thought to herself: you big child.

Monsieur Dunant's expression suddenly changed. His

look became tense, and had his wife not been sitting so close to him, he would have leaped up and paced about the room. Instead, he spoke from his chair. "You are right; I told Dr. Molard then that there would not be another war."

Madame interrupted. "And look what happened last year — 1848 was a year of rioting and fighting, the working people seemed to have gone mad with street fighting in all the major capitals of Europe!"

"In spite of all this," said Monsieur Dunant, "I still think people will come to their senses sometime and use the wonderful new inventions of this century to bring happiness and prosperity into the world, not use them for the destruction of mankind. It will take time, however; I was wrong twenty-one years ago when I thought it would happen immediately. But it will come, perhaps not in our lifetime, but in Henri's, or at least Henri's children will live to see it." Monsieur Dunant suddenly noticed that he had let his habit of preaching get the better of him, and pushing his wife gently away, he rose and walked over to the table.

"This subject should not make us forget the roses again today," he said. Taking one of the red roses out of the crystal vase, he pinned it to his wife's taffeta gown, using the silver pin which held her scarf in place. "Will you forgive my previous carelessness?" he asked.

"There is nothing to forgive, because it did not offend me. But this rose belongs to Henri. There are exactly twenty-one roses."

"He certainly won't count them. Besides, I think mothers should be more praised on their children's birthdays than the children themselves. That is why you should wear a rose today."

"Jean, have you got the ring?" Madame Dunant asked suddenly. "We keep on talking and Henri might be here any minute."

Monsieur Dunant took a small square box of blue leather from his pocket. "Here it is," he said, opening the case. The deep blue stone in the bright gold setting was embedded in folds of white satin.

"I've seen it, Jean, leave it closed." Madame Dunant was losing her patience. Taking the little box from her husband's hands, she put it underneath the roses, right in front of Henri's place. At that moment hurried footsteps could be heard in the hall and a happy voice called, "Mama, Papa!" The door was flung open and Henri rushed into the room.

Madame Dunant was surprised at the boisterous manner of her son, who generally was never loud. "Henri, please, wait a minute," she begged, but Henri paid no heed.

"Mama, Papa, do you know who is here?" he shouted. Without even waiting for an answer, he told them excitedly, "Michel!"

His parents did not seem to know whom he meant. Henri explained, "Michel Marouche! — Old Michel, who was in prison. I have told you of my success in converting a prisoner, haven't I? The prisoner was Michel. He has been set free. Two years of his term have been cancelled because of his good conduct. And he came here, the first thing he did, to tell me. Mama! Papa!"

There was a bright gleam in the eyes of the young Dunant. He resembled his father of twenty-one years ago, but the expression on his face was softer, more childlike than his father's had been, perhaps because Henri as yet wore no beard. The same determination was evident on the son's face, but his eyes were very dreamy and the arched eyebrows spoke of his vivid imagination. His father's once stern features had softened with kindness, whereas Henri's lips were thin and austere.

Henri Dunant did not make life easy for himself. At night he would often kneel for hours next to his bed in prayer, his tall figure bent low, his head on his knees. He belonged to a group of young men who had set for themselves the task of interesting rich people in the needs of the sick, the hungry, and the poor. Each one of the members of the "Society for Giving Alms" had been assigned a certain territory for works of Christian charity and mercy. They visited sick people and the poor families who lived in the tenements of the newly developed industrial areas, trying to bring them a little help and consolation. They called their visits "visitations," and on such visitations Henri had spent the larger part of his pocket money for the last three years. He would either buy food or give small donations: two francs here, five francs there. He thought about each need and planned his giving carefully, keeping a book of his "cases." On his own initiative, and representing the group, Henri spent every Sunday afternoon visiting the inmates of the Geneva prison. The prisoners were escorted to a room set aside for this purpose where, in a loud, preaching voice, he read passages to them from the Bible. He began to notice that the stories of the Old Testament were more pleasing than those of the New Testament; he therefore read more often of David and Goliath, of Moses and his law, and of the trials of Job. At the end he tried to explain the meaning of what he had just read, because he considered it necessary to relate the parables of the Old Testament to the everyday life of the prisoners. But he never seemed to find the right words. His own life was so different from theirs that he felt they were living on a far distant planet and when he tried to talk to them, his awareness of this difference overcame him. His words became empty, he felt they dropped off into space, and he would say a short prayer and start reading from a more worldly book. He brought along books on expeditions to foreign countries, about excavations in Egypt or about the original inhabitants of ancient Italy. It did not seem to matter what he read or how he spoke. It was important only that someone came to see them and talked to them. Sometimes Henri would look up from his book, right into their faces, but that was only occasionally, for most of the time his eyes would be fixed on the book he was holding in his hands, or on the floor. Their faces were tense, shy, indifferent, or blank. But once in a while a smile came to their eyes. Henri often wondered if they were smiling at what he was reading or if it was because of him and his zeal. He never knew, but he appreciated the smiles anyway.

He had noticed Michel Marouche from the very first time he had gone to the prison. His clothes and general appearance were the same as that of the other prisoners, but he alone would talk to Henri while the rest of the men preferred to step aside, unnoticed. Michel would step forward when Henri walked to the front of the room, his books under his arms, and speak up in the name of his "poor comrades." "You are a handsome young man, Monsieur. You are wonderful, Our Lord will bless you for your kindness," he would say. Henri had kept such words in his heart because he was not entirely free from vanity and pride.

And now Michel was set free, he was pardoned. Two years of his life were given back to him to live and enjoy. Although Henri did not say it out loud, he could not help thinking: this is to my credit.

"Papa, Mama, please, I would like to invite Michel to my birthday dinner."

"Of course, Henri, if it would please you," his mother acquiesced.

Suddenly they all became aware of the old man standing by the door, holding a small bundle in one hand and the doorknob in the other. His whole figure was slightly stooped and he had a long, thin neck; he looked somewhat like a bird. No one had heard him enter.

Monsieur Dunant approached him, holding his hand out.

"We are so glad that you want to spend this happy day with us, Monsieur Marouche. We would be delighted if you would share our simple meal."

This short speech would have been better suited to address the Mayor of Geneva than a released prisoner, but Monsieur Dunant felt rather uncomfortable and could think of nothing else to overcome this awkward moment.

Old Michel put his bundle down and reached for the outstretched hand. Now Madame Dunant also congratulated him on his release from prison. It made Henri very happy to see that Michel was trying to kiss his mother's hand, and that she did not withdraw it from him. She did feel it would be necessary, however, to have the old man change his clothes before sitting down at the table with the rest of the guests. He wore no coat, his rough shirt bore the black prison stamp on the chest, and his pants were of an undiscernible, washed-out color.

"Didn't you receive your own clothes back when you were released?" Madame Dunant inquired.

But Michel had an answer ready. With a disappointed smile he said, "No, Madame, they couldn't find my own clothes. They seem to have disappeared. I can't blame anybody, you know, not after twenty-three years. That was how long ago I had to take them off. The warden even looked for them himself; they simply couldn't be found." Looking from one person to the other, he put on a pathetic expression. "I had a nice blue coat, too. I used to like that coat, but they couldn't find that either."

"We will provide you with the necessary clothes," Madame Dunant said, opening the door and calling for Marie to come and take out Michel's bundle.

Monsieur Dunant asked to be excused. He had to attend to something in his room. Henri looked at his father gratefully; he could guesss what his father meant to do.

Madame left the room with Marie, and Henri and Michel were left alone. "How do you feel, my friend?" Henri asked the old man.

Shrugging his shoulders, Michel walked over to the dinner table. Stretching forward, he looked at every detail carefully.

"We are not supposed to look at it yet, Michel," Henri said. "But you'll sit next to me, I'll tell Marie to set one more place, for you." For the first time since Henri had known Michel, the old man seemed to be at a loss for words. Henri thought it might be due to his new freedom. That is why he asked: "Last Sunday, when I was with you, didn't you know then you would be released?"

"No, Monsieur, it came quite suddenly."

"Director Defour didn't say a word to me either."

"I suppose he wanted to keep it as a surprise for both of us. Yes, it certainly came as a surprise," he added after a short pause, and smiling slyly he continued, "Maybe it was meant as a sign of appreciation to you, a birthday present." And seeing that his idea was pleasing to Henri, he became his old talkative self again. "I am sure that's what it is. A sign of appreciation as a birthday gift, because you have always been so kind to the prisoners."

"It's my twenty-first birthday," Henri whispered. Michel caught his words.

"Well! Then, my special congratulations."

Henri was blushing, and in order to hide his happiness he said, "I'll go and tell Marie to set the table for one more guest, and to get one more chair, too."

"Please, don't worry so much over me, your old Michel."

"It is no trouble. I'll be back in a minute."

Monsieur Dunant was the first to return to the dining room. He was carrying a blue coat over his arm. He found the room empty. A breeze came in through the open windows, and the white curtains were swaying slightly. The scent of roses still filled the air. He was somewhat annoyed to find no one there because he had been hoping for a little sensation when he appeared with a blue coat for Michel. Putting the coat over a chair, he decided to wait. When no one came, he walked out into the hall where his wife, Henri and Marie were all busy, Marie with another setting of dishes.

"Where is Monsieur Marouche?" called Monsieur Dunant.

"I left him in the dining room," Henri answer. "Isn't he there?"

"No!"

"I presume he has gone to wash up," Madame Dunant decided. "He could stand it."

"Mama!"

They all went into the dining room and Marie started putting the extra plates on the table.

"I'd like him to sit next to me, please," Henri said, watching his parents' expression. "You don't mind, do you?" he asked. "It must be wonderful for him on his first day out, just like a birthday, like being born again."

"And to whom should he be grateful for this new life?" Madame Dunant inquired.

"Please, Mama, I have only done my duty."

"Well, I wish he was here now," Papa Dunant said. "Where in the world could he be so long?"

When Marie was through finishing the table and there was still no sign of Michel, Madame asked her to go and look for him. Marie returned in a little while and said that she could not find him anywhere, but that François had seen the old man leave through the garden gate, in quite a hurry.

"Is his bundle still here?" Henri asked, upset by this news.

"Yes, his bundle is still in the hall where I put it," Marie answered.

"He can't have left then," Henri sighed in relief. "I wouldn't know why . . . " and suddenly he thought of Kurtli and the little incident with the coat so long ago. He remembered that Kurtli had been embarrassed to accept his gift. He realized how difficult it is for a wealthy person to help someone who is poor.

"But I am afraid I know why," Henri's father said, pressing his lips together excitedly. "Marie, please go and call everybody to dinner. Uncle David will be here any minute."

"You don't think . . ." escaped from Madame's lips.

What relief, what he was looking for was there. Monsieur held the little blue leather case in his hand. "I am sorry, Henri, for showing this to you before the time. I wish you could have found it underneath the roses, but I was afraid . . ."

Henri opened the case, but the box was empty. There was no ring in the folds of the white silk lining.

" . . . and I was right," Monsieur Dunant said slowly.

From that moment on, Henri was no longer a child.

CHAPTER FOUR

1859

The doorbell of "La Monaie" had rung almost steadily since early morning. The most prominent families in Geneva had sent servants to the Dunant house to deliver boxes and cartons of all sizes and shapes, as well as huge baskets of flowers.

There were hothouse lilacs, roses, tulips and hyacinths, some with elaborate satin ribbon bows. Bottles were packed into gift boxes: wines and cordials, the very best cognac and champagne. Tied to the flowers or buried in the green shredded paper around the bottles were little envelopes, and most of these envelopes carried this message:

"Best Wishes for a Happy Birthday to the General Manager."

Marie, standing in the hall, received the presents and handed them to François and a second butler, hired for the occasion, who carried them into the reception room. Madame Dunant waited there to supervise the display of presents. French doors had been opened to make one large room out of the salon and the dining room, and a table had been set for twenty-four guests. Along the wall behind the dinner table the flowers were arranged on a long, narrow sideboard and on small, velvet-covered tables brought in for the day. On the floor were boxes, open to disclose the bottles they contained.

From time to time, Monsieur Dunant stopped at the reception room to check on the preparations. His wife kept assuring him that men were only in the way at such a time, but when he got past her guard, he went straight to the rows of presents. He took one bottle after another from its bed of tissue paper and held it up against the light, admiring its amber, yellow, green or red contents. Reading the labels, he smiled and said,

"What a lucky boy! I have never in my life seen such a birthday table."

Madame Dunant seemed too busy and preoccupied to show any pleasure.

On one of his visits during the afternoon, Monsieur Dunant found a few figurines of Meissen porcelain on a small table. There were ladies in hoop skirts and gentlemen in cutaways, all of whom had little cards inscribed "To the

General Manager" dangling from their arms. Monsieur Dunant frowned, saying to his wife:

"Anne, I know this porcelain. I'm sure I have seen it before."

Madame Dunant shook her head and nodded toward the servants who were at work setting the table. Monsieur Dunant walked to the window. The trees in the garden were showing off their spring foliage, still more yellow than green. When the servants were out of earshot, he said:

"I don't think it is necessary to pretend that Henri has even more presents than were really sent, Anne. Aren't there enough without this deception?"

"There were not enough," she whispered, "and I *do* think it is necessary. It is necessary for Henri's business. If we do not put on a display, his associates will believe the stories which are going around that Henri's African business is weak — that his shares are insecure. That is the reason for this whole show, for the orchids at 12 francs 50 apiece. Prestige is a vital part of business."

"I prefer honest roses, or even daisies, to orchids whose sole purpose is to look important." Monsieur Dunant left the room.

In the meantime, François had placed a silver basket full of yellow roses with the other presents. Madame Dunant stepped over to it.

"Who sent these roses?" she asked, counting them in her head. . . . twenty-eight, twenty-nine, thirty. Thirty! She thought — one is missing. Henri is thirty-one today.

"These flowers were sent by His Excellency, General de Beaufort," François answered.

"So he didn't forget, although he was preparing to leave the country." Madame was delighted at this evidence of the General's thought for her son.

The General had departed with a French force to support the Italians in their fight for unification. Several Italian states had rebelled against their Austrian overlords, and France was backing them up in their efforts to make Italy one country, independent of Austrian domination. Italy's long history of warring, separate city-states made their struggle the more difficult, even though France (then under Napoleon III) was committed to the Italian side.

"You can't put *this* arrangement on the floor," Madame Dunant said. "Bring in a stand for the General's roses."

Once the flowers were placed on the stand, she stood back to admire them. Her husband, having returned to the room, determined to take their own porcelain figurines from the display of presents, stood in the door.

"Look, from General de Beaufort! Isn't it a beautiful arrangement? I always knew that he was a man of culture and aristocratic taste."

"Culture, taste," muttered Monsieur Dunant. "He shows his culture by becoming a professional soldier, going to war and killing other people for a living. That is his 'tasteful' occupation."

"But how often does a war occur?" asked Madame. "Once or twice during a lifetime, perhaps."

"And for being true to his real vocation — killing innocent people once or twice in a lifetime — he is paid a
princely salary all his life. He even draws a pension for his
bloody work."

Madame fidgeted with her scarf. "Why do you always
look at things from such an unpatriotic angle, Jean? Who
is he fighting now, anyway? Croats, Austrians, or something like that?"

Madame turned the card a little, so that the golden letters could be read easily by visitors.

"To the General Manager with my most sincere good
wishes, General de Beaufort."

The hero of the occasion, for whom all these preparations were made, had so far escaped all the bustle. Henri
had received the birthday wishes of his family at breakfast,
and since then had been working in his room. Late in the
afternoon, his mother knocked at the door.

"Henri, please get dressed," she said. "We expect the
first guests any minute." Madame was wearing an evening
dress of changeable green and blue silk which rustled as
she moved.

"You look beautiful, Mama," Henri said, as he bent to
kiss his mother's cheek. "But I am not finished with my
work," he added, looking at the papers which covered
his desk.

Madame Dunant smiled at him. "Entertaining your
stockholders is part of your work, too. It's not a simple matter, even if they are coming to celebrate your birthday."
She smiled at her son.

"You are right, of course, Mama."

As Madame had foreseen, the first carriages were arriving. Henri, from his window, watched the elaborately dressed guests walk up the path and disappear into the house. François, holding a silver candelabra, led them up to the entrance.

It certainly was time for Henri to get dressed. Walking toward the mirror, he tied his white tie around his stiff collar. He changed his coat and brushed back his dark hair. Smoothing down his mustache, Henri looked approvingly at himself in the mirror. He left his room and walked slowly down the stairs, leaning over the carved bannister to observe the crowd gathering underneath the crystal chandeliers. The white-haired gentleman must be General Defour, and the lady by his side could only be Madame Ivry, widow of the famous banker, Jacques Ivry.

When Henri joined the company, he immediately became the focus of attention. The young general manager bowed in all directions, kissed the ladies' hands and shook the gentlemen's.

"Well, you African adventurer, how do you like being back in our northern climate?"

"How was Tunis? I hear you spent the winter there."

"Are our mills still clattering?" asked Madame Ivry, a stockholder of Mills Incorporated of Mons-Djemila. Cleverly, Madame Dunant changed the subject so that Henri did not have to discuss business so early in the evening.

When François announced the last guests, Madame Dunant asked her son to lead her into the dining room. The other couples followed. Talking and laughing, they entered the lavishly decorated room, and the ladies could hardly refrain from outbursts of enthusiasm. However, in nineteenth century Geneva, with its Calvinistic tradition, any comment on such extravagance would have been considered to be evidence of poor breeding. Some of the guests — the new rich of their century — had never before seen such a display of china, silver and crystal, and certainly never such a magnificent group of presents, but they all imitated the cool restraint of the aristocrats who were present and refrained from comment on the display.

After the speeches and the toasts expressing the good wishes of the company toward Henri Dunant, the atmosphere around the long table became relaxed. Conversation turned to business, and particularly to the business affairs of Mills Incorporated of Mons-Djemila, of which Henri Dunant was president and general manager. Most of the shares of Mills, Inc., worth five hundred thousand francs, were owned by the people present.

"Far be it from me to express the slightest lack of confidence in you, especially today," remarked Count Budé to his host. "However, years have gone by since you first applied for the right to buy twelve hundred acres of land on the African river Oned Saf Saf. These years have drained the resources of our company, since more money can be lost under the hot African sun in a day than can be earned in a year in our cooler North."

The Count had tried to be careful in his choice of words, but his statement spelled mistrust. The whole company had heard him, and the atmosphere became tense. Madame Dunant's smile was stiff.

"What do *you* intend to do?" Madame Ivry turned to the man on her right, Monsieur Guerland, owner of some of Geneva's largest silk factories and a shrewd businessman. No one had ever heard Guerland make a false prediction or an unsuccessful speculation.

"First of all," he laughed, "I'll have another glass." He helped himself from a tray.

"No doubt," said Madame Ivry, "you have every reason to be in a good mood."

"I do, I do. I hired my sixtieth weaver yesterday. I'll soon have to open up another plant."

"Is it possible?" Madame Ivry pretended to be stunned, although nothing happened in Geneva that she did not know about.

"Yes," answered Monsieur Guerland proudly.

"How do you do it?"

"I don't do anything. My nose for business does it all." He was laughing again as he emptied his glass. His nose did indeed show all the work it had to do; it was big and swollen.

"And what does your nose say about Dunant?" asked Madame quietly. Guerland looked around, but nobody seemed to be listening to their conversation. He shook his head, a worried expression on his face.

"My nose tells me to withdraw."

"And will you do so?"

"I must, if my nose tells me. 'Draw back,' it says. Don't

you understand? So what else can I do? I have to draw back."

"Yes, yes," nodded Madame Ivry. "You are always right." As it became obvious that the guests were interested in nothing but the mills of Mons-Djemila and the African affairs of the corporation, Henri decided that he must make a statement on the subject. He rose from his seat at the end of the table.

"My dear friends, ladies and gentlemen," he began. He had never been a good public speaker, and the fact made his mother nervous. She beckoned to the waiters to stop serving. Although Henri spoke timidly, pausing between every word, the noise along the table was hushed the minute he started his speech.

"My friends, you have presented me with many beautiful gifts. I hope you will allow me to present you with a little pleasure in return. I am privileged to bring you news which equals a gift of gold. In just a few weeks, I shall have the government permit necessary to purchase the African land. Nothing can stop us from buying the acreage we need. Thanks to your investments, the money is available and the plans have been ready for a long time; we can begin immediately to build additional mills. We can sow corn over a distance farther than the eye can see. I visualize the golden corn swaying in the wind; then the wagons, piled high, bringing the rich harvest to our mills. I can see a white stream of flour leaving our mills again. Bag after bag will be sold to the French Colonial Army, who will be happy to buy our local flour in place of the expensive flour imported from Europe that they have been using."

Count Budé interrupted. "What makes you think we will get the permit so soon?"

"I was able to get an audience with the French commander in Algiers, General MacMahon. General de Beaufort, whom we are proud to claim as a member of our board, introduced me to him. A gracious letter from MacMahon then introduced me to the commander in Constantine, General Gastu." Dunant then described his friendly conversation with Gastu, bringing in every detail he could remember. As he spoke, he imperceptibly crossed the border between reality and imagination. Henri talked as if the general had offered him something solid instead of the hopes he built up in his daydreams under the hot African sun. As he continued, he grew more secure with every new promise he made. His guests, listening attentively, could almost see gold pouring down on their heads.

"What do you think now?" asked Madame Ivry of Monsieur Guerland.

"I stick to my opinion." Monsieur helped himself to dessert. "I regret not having invested more heavily in the mills."

"But you just said ... "

The general manager finished his speech and resumed his seat next to his mother. The gay noise had quieted down, and Madame Dunant raised her voice.

"Let that be the end of all business conversation, please.

It almost turned a birthday party into a board meeting."

"Pardon me, Madame, for being the one to deny you this request." Count Budé rose from his seat again. "Unfortunately, I have had news which is less pleasant than our president's message. I have been informed by an associate of Count Chasseloup-Laubat, Secretary of Colonial Affairs, that the territory in question has been granted to a certain Rousset, who put in a claim for it only a few weeks ago. As you all know, Monsieur Dunant has been promising for years to get this grant for Mons-Djemila."

The room was so still that the guests could be heard breathing.

"I'm inclined to assume that this serious fact has so far been unknown to our active, and otherwise well-informed president." The count took his seat again.

"Did you know that, Henri?" whispered Madame Dunant.

Once more Madame Ivry asked Guerland: "What does your nose say now?"

The whispering stopped when the young president rose again to his feet. "The facts which Count Budé presented were as much of a surprise to me as they were to you. And I do not doubt them — as some of you may — but I tell you," and his voice became louder and more convincing — "I tell you that not even these facts can change the situation as I described it to you a few minutes ago."

"Cannot change the situation?" The count rose so abruptly that his chair toppled over with a crash.

Again the room became completely quiet. Henri took

a folded manuscript from his pocket, and the rustle of its pages was the only sound. Not even Madame Dunant knew what her son would do, and Monsieur Guerland was unable to satisfy Madame Ivry's curiosity. The general manager unfolded his papers and began to read off the title of his manuscript:

"The Re-established Empire of Charlemagne, or the Holy Roman Empire, Restored By His Majesty Emperor Napoleon III; by Henri Dunant, Director and President of Mills Incorporated of Mons-Djemila, Member of the French-Oriental Society, the Geographical Societies of Paris and Geneva, the Historical Society of Algiers, etc. etc. . . . "

Dunant droned on, and the count interrupted him. "All very well, but what does this historical treatise have to do with the African grant?"

Henri smiled, feeling triumphant.

"This 'historical treatise' will be submitted to the Emperor by me, during a private audience. It contains proof that the Roman Empire has never ceased to exist, and that Napleon III is its legitimate head. I do not doubt that His Majesty, after reading my paper, will grant us the concessions or anything else we desire."

"But the Secretary of the Colonies . . ."

"The Emperor, whose approval I expect to win, is still superior to the Secretary!"

The Count produced another objection to Henri's dreams. "I do not know whether our general manager is aware of the fact that the Emperor is on his way to the Italian war at this moment. I don't know . . ."

"I do know," Henri interrupted. "I know all of that. But what is to stop me from going to the Italian front myself to meet the Emperor? Crowned with the laurels of his victory, Napoleon III will be all the more willing to grant our petition."

"Child, think of the dangers!"

"I fear no danger but the danger of losing, through timidity and pessimism, the capital entrusted to me."

Enthusiastic applause followed. The buoyancy and extravagance of the young president charmed his audience. Even if his "treatise" was nothing but shrewd flattery, they all knew that the Emperor was susceptible to flattery. That was the way to success! The guests rose to their feet and cheered their host.

"What do you say now?" Madame Ivry no longer felt obliged to lower her voice.

"I shall stick to my opinion." Monsieur Guerland emptied his drink and remained standing after the others had taken their seats. Tapping a silver spoon against a glass, he demanded attention for his next words, in which he expressed his desire to double the capital of the corporation by signing new shares. Madame Dunant was the first to take up his idea and suggested:

"Whoever objects to the proposal of the distinguished and experienced Monsieur Guerland will rise, please."

No one rose. Only Count Budé turned to François and asked for his coat. The rest of the guests lingered to talk and to congratulate their host. When they left at last, and only the family remained, Henri said:

"You deserve a medal, Mama."

"Then give me one," laughed his mother.

Taking an envelope from one of the baskets of flowers, Henri tied it around his mother's neck with its silver cord. The card, dangling over her heart, read: "To the General Manager!"

"I don't want to be general manager if it means I must go to the Italian war. Neither do I want you to go."

Monsieur Dunant asked: "Do you really want to chase the French Emperor to his cursed war?"

"Yes, Papa," Henri answered. After a short pause he added: "I have no choice."

CHAPTER FIVE

1862

The sunny side of the Rue Saint Pierre felt extremely pleasant after the wet, cold April which Geneva had suffered. On the shady side the pavement was chilly and damp, so barefoot children from the country, in town to sell their violets, tried to stay in the sun.

"Violets! Buy my violets!" "Only ten centimes, Madame!" they called, holding out their little baskets full of purple blossoms and dark green leaves.

"Violets, violets!"

They ran after potential customers, keeping on until they sold their flowers or until it was obvious that they

58

were not wanted. They had very little trouble disposing of the flowers, for the children were persistent and city people like to buy violets when the sun is out at last after a spell of rainy weather.

The most easily persuaded customer of the afternoon stopped as soon as the first basket was held out to him. His was a tall, bent figure, and he looked at the children with sad eyes which glowed large and dark in his pale face.

"Please buy some violets," said little Blanche, looking up at the stranger. Usually the most timid of children, she was not afraid of this man. When his shaking hands had chosen one bunch from Blanche's baskets, the other children came running up to him. He took a bunch from each child, but still they did not let him go. They kept begging him to take more, trying to find out how many they could sell to this funny man. Soon he noticed that the children were laughing at him, and he said, as if to explain himself:

"It's my birthday today."

He looked carefully at the children. There were boys and girls, fair-haired and dark ones, tall ones and short ones, but they were all from poor families. They would not know how happy a birthday could be to the child of a wealthy family.

"When I was your age, I used to get a birthday cake with a candle on it for every year of my age, and the same number of roses. Every year, another candle and another rose . . . ." To the children, it sounded like a fairy tale.

"Won't you have a birthday cake today, Monsieur?" asked

Blanche, her face as worried as if it were her own birthday passing without notice.

He shook his head and smiled sadly.

"And no roses either?" asked the little girl.

"I don't think so."

"Then you must buy yourself as many bunches of violets as you should have roses and candles," said one of the bolder boys. Some of the other children, especially the girls, were ashamed of the suggestion. This was really taking advantage of the stranger. But when they saw that he smiled at the idea, they crowded around him, calling: "Yes! Yes! Buy them from me! How many do you need?"

"We'll carry them for you. We'll carry them!"

"I have an empty basket," said Blanche. The gentleman put his flowers into her basket, then added more bunches until he had thirty-four.

"One more, one more," begged the children.

"No, that's enough now. Do I look older than that?"

The children did not answer. Some rearranged their baskets; others were counting their money and tying it into handkerchiefs. Soon they skipped away, but the biggest boy turned and shouted over his shoulder: "Yes, much older! Like an old, old man."

The children disappeared until only little Blanche, holding the basket with the thirty-four bunches, was still standing beside the lonely looking stranger. Slowly, with short steps, he resumed his walk up the Rue Saint Pierre. The little girl tiptoed behind him, carrying the basket as if it were a valuable burden.

When they had almost reached the cathedral, the gentleman stopped in front of a big door and turned to his companion. She was still afraid to look at him because she felt so ashamed of her friends. He said:

"This is where I live. What are we going to do with all these violets? I wish they were still on the meadow."

"They grow near the woods," said Blanche, blushing again.

"I wish they were there, their roots still in the damp soil."

"Yes, they do like damp soil." The child added quickly, "But they all belong to you now, because you bought them."

The stranger realized that Blanche would never understand his belief that flowers could not be bought with money. He felt that it was wrong to reward with money those who picked flowers.

His train of thought led him to war and soldiers. He pressed his hands against his temples, hoping to hold back the thoughts that threatened to burst from his head. Human beings, as well as violets, were torn from the soil in which they grew, separated from their families and friends by a cruel hand. What, after all, were the regiments and battalions but bunches of flowers, tied together by forced patriotism and thrown away when they withered and died. When the swollen tongues of the wounded cried for water, and their cries rang through the night — as he himself could bear witness — they could be compared to dead stalks of flowers, tossed away by a callous hand. The hand that picked the flowers — or bought them — was the hand that forced men into war; the generals, the stockholders in munitions plants, the war administrations in every capital of the world; all these had a hand in the devastation.

The stranger traced a violent gesture through the air, as if to strike an end to horror. When he saw the little girl start back in fear, he realized that he was not on a battlefield but on the Rue Saint Pierre in Geneva.

"Carry these flowers to the church. I can't look at them." Seeing the disappointed look in the child's eyes, he took one bunch from the basket.

"Now carry the rest to the church."

The little girl curtsied and ran toward the church without looking behind her.

Henri Dunant opened the big door and walked up a wooden staircase. Every time he passed a window he rested, looking at the chestnut tree outside. As he climbed, he seemed to be ascending its branches, as free as the woodpecker, the blackbird and the sparrow whom he had envied as they enjoyed their tree.

When he reached the door of his room he stopped long enough to catch his breath, then he turned the knob. His door was never locked. Sunlight poured through the open window, shining right on his desk, and there among its papers and books stood a crystal vase of roses which had not been there when he had left the room. The draft of the open door and window carried a strong perfume, the scent of his childhood birthdays. Dunant did not have to count the roses, for he knew that there were thirty-four and he knew who had brought them. As he stepped into the room, a rosy-faced, white-haired woman slipped from behind the door and threw her arms around his neck.

"Mama." He pulled his mother close and kissed her cheeks. Tears of emotion stood in his eyes, for he had not seen a member of his family for weeks. He had moved to his lonely room to avoid inflicting on others the nervous outbreaks to which he had been subject since his return from Italy. Also, he had not wished to be disturbed in his all-important work.

Henri was about to hand his mother the bunch of violets he had bought in the street when a sharp pain forced him to gasp and bend over.

"What is the matter? For Heaven's sake!"

His mother helped him over to the couch. Henri lay down, holding his hands to his stomach.

"Is it your stomach? Can I give you anything?" Madame looked frantically around her son's simple room.

"No, it is — the liver. There are drops over there, on the table."

Walking over to the table, Madame asked: "Have you had attacks like this before, then?" She carried the bottle to the window and read the inscription.

"Yes," said Henri softly. He did not want to upset his mother, but neither did he want to tell her a lie. "Yes, since Italy. The attacks must be caused by the bad water we drank there, or by the lack of decent food during the weeks I spent in the church where we had our headquarters. In the Chiesa Maggiore, there were no luxuries and few necessities. They may even be caused by the disgust and anger I felt in those days when I was so near the battle-field and could do so little to help the suffering men."

"I suppose, then, that this is another 'Souvenir of Solferino'?"

At his mother's words, Henri turned still more ashen. She had betrayed her knowledge of his most precious secret, confirming his sick suspicion that the world was spying on him. He jumped up and rushed to his desk. To his horror, the notes had been shuffled.

"The statistics are irreplaceable," he cried, almost in hysterics. "Do you realize that only the kindness and generosity of the French government has let me have copies of these maps? If one sheet is missing or damaged, the work of months is lost! Oh, and here, the list of those who helped me in the Chiesa Maggiore — on the floor!" Taking up the loose pages from the floor, he clutched them to his chest.

"Leave me, leave me alone!" he cried, pointing to the open door. But Madame Dunant had control of herself, and her son's despair did not disturb her poise. She walked over to the door and closed it, and the room became cold and dim. His mother's calm and determination took the last shred of Henri's dignity, and he sobbed as helplessly as a child.

"You come only to spy on me — to find out what I am working on. You read my manuscript!" he cried, withdrawing to the furthest corner.

"You are crazy, Henri," his mother said coldly. "I did

not come here to spy, or read your insane scribbles, but to bring you roses for your birthday."

"Take them back again," he screamed. "I don't want your roses. They are nothing but a way to intrude into my peace!" Struck by pain again, he fell back on the couch, hiding his face underneath the rough blanket.

The old lady's lips quivered as she watched her son. How right you are, Henri, she thought. The roses were only a means to get to see you. I did not come here to read your silly scribble about Solferino; I came to call you back into the real world. I want you back on the road to success and wealth once more, on the road along which you were advancing when you got lost in this jungle of crazy ideas.

Madame Dunant put the bottle of medicine back on the table and went over to the couch. The slender man pushed the papers under his blanket and put his arms over his face. His shaking back betrayed what he wanted to hide: he was sobbing.

His mother tried a different approach. Sitting on the bed, she softly stroked his hair, which was long and neglected. His collar — her own responsibility for years — was none too clean. We will become an object of ridicule for all Geneva, a disgrace for the whole Dunant family, she thought. But aloud she said,

"My poor child, everyone has to see horrible and cruel things at some time during his life. We can't keep the memory of them before our eyes — nobody could live that way. Nature never meant us to bury ourselves in our own sorrows, much less those of others. Forget what you have seen in Italy. Time will help you, time and some sensible occupation. Devote yourself to your business again, that business which was once so successful."

Henri was quiet once more, and Madame believed herself successful. "See," she said, "now you are trying to be sensible. You must forget, if you are going to live. Forget the past, and forget your 'Souvenir of Solferino.' "

Madame Dunant was so convinced of her victory that she spoke these words in mocking tones. It was a great mistake. Henri jumped up and shouted:

"No, no, never!"

Henri stared into his mother's face; he was deathly pale. His eyes were red and his hair disorderly. After a few seconds of silence, during which mother and son stared at each other, Henri said calmly:

"No, Mama, I will not forget. I do not want to forget. I shall never forget June 24th, 1859, and I shall not forget Solferino. Some day, those who read my book will not be able to forget Solferino either."

His mother moved away a little, with a look of assumed interest. "What is this Solferino, anyway, Henri? Some little Italian town, that's all."

"Before June 24th, 1859, Solferino was nothing but a little village — you are right so far, Mama. It was a small town in Lombardy, with whitewashed houses, green vineyards and red roofs. Peaceful people lived a peaceful life there, full of joy and sorrow, gossip and scandal. Children were born, and old people died.

"After June 24th, it was quite different. By evening of that dreadful day the white houses had collapsed, and their burnt-out ruins stood pointing to the sky, from which rain poured steadily. Gardens and fields were destroyed; corn and oats were trampled down; hedges and vineyards were devastated. Dead soldiers lay in gutters, in the fields, anywhere. The wounded also lay there, because there was nobody to pick them up and carry them to the shelter of a roof. Their blood mingled with the rain, and only the night heard their cries. Certainly the villagers did not dare to help them; they feared that if they left their dugouts they would be caught and shot as spies. There were reports that the victorious French would return; that the Austrians were preparing a counterattack. Fear had closed the shelters that existed, and the wounded were left outside in the rain and the night without help or consolation. The number of the injured ran as high as forty thousand."

Henri was silent. After a while, his mother asked:

"And there was nobody to help?"

"Nobody," he answered. The vision of war rose again before his eyes. "Nobody, till I came running down from the hill from which I had watched the battle since early morning. That day I wore a ridiculous white suit, which I did not take off for the next few weeks — not even once! The Italians called me 'l'uomo bianco,' the Man in White. How ironic to think that I wore that suit to avoid being taken for a spy or anyone concerned with the battle!"

"It was none of your concern."

Henri did not hear his mother. "I did not know then that the costume which I wore so that I would not be taken for a soldier would one day be a uniform."

"You did not wear a uniform," Madame tried again. "You had nothing to do with that war. For the last time, you were on a business trip!"

"We all have to do with war, Mama, when our brothers are being killed."

"Foreign soldiers," Madame Dunant snorted. "Austrians . . . Croats . . . God knows who . . . "

"All my brothers!" Henri was regaining his strength. "Tutti fratelli — we are all brothers — was our password at Chiesa Maggiore. Croats, Frenchmen, Italians, Austrians, yes! But each one of them was a human being; very often not much more than a heap of burned flesh, but yet, a human being. Every one of them had a mother, for whom he cried in his agony. Every one of them was thirsty and hungry. The French had started the battle with nothing in their stomachs but a cup of strong black coffee and the Austrians had been issued nothing but a double ration of strong liquor. None of the soldiers had a bite of bread during the whole dreadful day, in order that the armies would fight more desperately. Those forty thousand men at Solferino suffered torturing pain, and every one of them needed bandages, gauze and linen. I heard every one of them curse the war. Forty thousand men were cursing war in every language of Europe, Mother, and the sound still rings in my ears.

"Every one of that forty thousand was in need of consolation; every one in need of a brother to lift him up from the muddy soil. I saw forty thousand men lying before me, and realized that I was alone. We were forty thousand wounded, the night and I, and in the distance, the ruins of Solferino, from which not a single light could be seen. That is my memory; that is my Solferino, Mama."

When Henri had finished speaking, the room became depressingly quiet. Only the buzzing of a bee caught behind the curtains could be heard. The sun had wandered, too, and its rays fell into the room on a long slant, sending the shadow of the windowframe in a zig-zag pattern over the white boards of the floor.

Madame Dunant took up the conversation cautiously. "All this is horrible, Henri. I know how sensitive you are, and how an experience of this kind must weigh on your mind. But you must force yourself to face the fact that there will always be another Solferino, because there will always be another war."

"There will be other wars, but there should be no other Solferino." Henri was agitated again, and he jerked his notes from under the blanket. Looking through them for a particular passage, he said: "Everything — *everything* — must be done to help the wounded, with no thought of their nationality. Nurses and doctors must be neutral; a relief and rescue service must be initiated; these people must be protected by an insignia which both sides will recognize."

Henri found the passage he wanted and began to read, so that his mother was the first to hear the message which was about to galvanize the world's conscience.

"An appeal has to go out, a plea must be made to the people of all countries and classes, to the powerful of this world and to the lowest working men, so that every one of them, in his own manner, in his particular field and in accordance with his means, may take part in his project. . . .

"A congress must be held to establish some kind of international, legitimate and sacred declaration which, once agreed upon and ratified, will serve as a basis for an organization to aid all the wounded . . . .

"Humanity and civilization demand such an undertaking. Which sovereign, which potentate, would deny assistance to such an organization?

"Even if the terrible weapons at the disposal of all nations nowadays will in all probability shorten future wars, the battles will, nevertheless, be all the more murderous . . . .

"Are not such considerations alone sufficient reason to prepare against disaster?"

Henri finished reading, his arms dropped, and the papers fell to the floor beside the couch. He looked at his mother, but she said nothing. At that moment, Henri realized that she was old. Deep lines around her eyes lent a tired expression to her face. Slight creases at the corners of her mouth had been carved by disappointments. He was struck all of a sudden by sympathy toward this strange old lady — no longer the remembered mother of his childhood — who sat beside him, tears running down her powdered face. Drawing her hands to him, he kissed them.

"Mama, are you crying? Does the soldiers' fate touch you? Do you understand me now?"

"I can see now where you are going," she replied.

Henri rose. All timidity, fatigue and desperation seemed to have fled. His back against the window, he looked at his mother, and the sunlight framed his dark silhouette.

"I, too, can see where I am going. I am going to the courts of Europe, and I shall put my message in front of the monarchs. My 'Souvenir of Solferino' shall lie on top of the documents of the Secretaries of War. I shall go to everyone with any power at all; I shall go to all conventions; I shall go. . ."

"You are going into poverty, Henri," his mother interrupted. Her voice shook, and she looked sadly into his dark eyes, now full of determination. "You are going into poverty, and we shall all be made to suffer with you."

CHAPTER SIX

1865

Anyone could tell that May 8th, 1865, was a Sunday just by watching the people strolling through the streets in their best clothes. Everyone seemed to have plenty of time to exchange friendly smiles, kind words, and laughter. It was a lovely spring day. A soft, new breeze stirred the tender young leaves; white and purple lilacs had opened up during the night, and their fragrance was in the air. Jubilant bells rang from the tower of the cathedral and could even be heard out in the residential suburbs of the city.

Henri Dunant was not paying attention to the bells, however. He was too busy watering the plants on the win-

72

dow sill of his room. He walked from one pot to another with a little can in his hands, giving each plant its share of water. The black soil of the fern drank up the water with a gurgling sound, for it loved moisture. He did not water the cactus every day, for its homeland was hot, dry and sandy but today he gave it some water, and some also to the Monstera that needed care only once a week.

Monsieur Dunant began to untie the red ribbon which held the tender stem of the orange tree to its supporting stick when someone knocked on the door.

"Come in," Monsieur Dunant called, without looking around. He heard the door opening and closing, but no one spoke, so he turned around. A small, slender boy stood waiting by the door. His blond hair had been combed with a wet comb, his freckled face had been scrubbed until it shone. His thin arms were holding a bunch of letters, and he had a small white box in one hand.

"The mail, Uncle Henri," the boy said, stepping closer to Monsieur Dunant.

"Well, why are you bringing the mail today, Reni?" Monsieur asked, putting down the pitcher. He took the bundle of letters from the child, who immediately hid the hand holding the box behind his back.

"I met François on the stairs. He was just on his way up with the mail. So I asked him to let me bring it; I was coming up anyway." Reni stood erect near Monsieur's desk as he spoke, but Monsieur was already so occupied with the letters that he no longer paid much attention to the boy. He carefully opened the envelopes with an ivory letter

opener. Some of the envelopes were long and narrow, some
were short; there were tan ones, gray ones, blue ones, and
many white ones.

"What kind of a stamp is this, Uncle Henri? Where does
this letter come from?" Reni leaned over the desk and
pointed to an extra large blue stamp. Monsieur was just
about to put it with the rest of the letters, because he preferred to open them all first before he read any. He picked
up the letter with the large stamp.

"This one comes from Spain," he replied.

Reni was thrilled. He had never before seen a stamp
that size. That would be a wonderful stamp for his collec-
tion if only he dared ask Monsieur Dunant for it. Monsieur
was not his real uncle, however; in fact, Reni's father was
the gardener for "La Monaie," so Reni did not feel free
to ask for the stamp. He said instead, "Who is the lady on
this stamp?"

"That is Queen Isabella. Count Ripalda in Madrid sent
me this letter," Monsieur said, reading the address on the
back of the envelope.

"Do you know a count?" Reni's voice was filled with
awe.

"Certainly," Monsieur Dunant answered and he smiled
as he thought of how many people of rank he knew:
counts, barons, dukes, even emperors and kings. And they
had all congratulated him on his work; well, almost all of
them.

Meanwhile Reni had picked up another envelope. "This

is another one from Spain. Look, it has the same large blue stamp."

He was right. The return address on this one said Dr. Landa.

"Dr. Landa," Monsieur Dunant said to himself and his open, child-like face, lit up. "A smart man with a warm heart. He was the representative of the Spanish throne when our Convention was signed."

"Did he come here, to Geneva, just to sign his name?" wondered Reni.

"Yes. He came to testify by his signature, for all of Spain, that in case of war his country would recognize the arrangements of the International Committee of Geneva: protection to the nursing staff of the enemy, care of the wounded of one's own country and of the enemy . . . But you know all this."

"Yes, I do," Reni answered. He had been told the statutes of the Convention of Geneva more than once by Henri Dunant. He almost knew the ten articles by heart. But right now the foreign stamps were far more interesting to him. Taking up another letter, he tried to identify the head on the stamp.

"That is Wilhelm I, King of Prussia," Monsieur explained.

"How do you know?" the boy asked.

"I happen to know His Majesty," Monsieur assured him.

"You really know him?"

"Yes."

"Have you ever talked to him?"

"Yes."

"What did he say?"

" 'Good evening, Monsieur,' " he said.

"No!" Reni could not believe that a king would simply say, "Good evening Monsieur."

"Oh, yes." Monsieur Dunant was pleased to see the boy's amazement, and he continued, "and then the king said: 'I am glad that you have come to Berlin to see us.' "

Reni's face showed his astonishment and excitement and Monsieur, glad of an approving audience, continued, "That was not all His Majesty had to say. He also said, 'You are undertaking a very noble work, which deserves every possible help.' "

Monsieur Dunant was once more overwhelmed by a wonderful sensation as he repeated these words that he had heard in almost all the capitals of Europe. He had gone to Berlin, to Dresden, to Vienna and to Munich to ask that a representative of each government come to the congress in Geneva. The officials he had seen had raised their eyebrows in astonishment at the unruly young man and asked what sort of congress it would be. He had answered that it would be a congress of all those who wished to examine the proposals of the relief committee of Geneva, who wished to assume responsibility for the wounded soldiers and sign an international agreement to that effect. The officials had asked who was backing such an agreement, what political power stood behind such an idea. And Dunant had answered, "Merely five Swiss citizens, all private persons. I am one of them. I am Henri Dunant, author of the book *Souvenir of Solferino*."

Many of the Secretaries recognized the title of the book and received him warmly because of it. His book had prepared the way for him; it opened the doors to the European courts and to their kings.

The monarchs chose the delegates who came to the preliminary conference on October 26th, 1863, and then to the signing of the Geneva Convention on August 22nd, 1864. Each country had thereby accepted the requirements and provisos suggested by *Souvenir of Solferino* and formulated by the board of five citizens of Geneva: Henri Dunant, Gustave Moynier, General Defour, Dr. Appia, and Dr. Maunoir.

Reni put the letter from Prussia carefully against the back of the desk.

"Why do you put that letter apart?" Monsieur asked.

"I want to keep the kings you know together, right here," answered Reni.

"Very well," Monsieur agreed. He took up another letter.

"I am sure you know this gentleman yourself," he said, handing the envelope to Reni. The stamp was green with a picture of a distinguished man in uniform on it. Reni frowned and shook his head. He peered closely at the stamp and found the word "France" on the edge of it.

"Oh, that is Napoleon III, the Emperor of France."

"You see, you did recognize him."

"Yes, but I have never talked with him."

"Neither have I. He has answered my letters and peti-
tions through his secretary, but I have never personally
spoken with the Emperor of France. At one time . . ." He
broke off his sentence, for he had begun to say that he had
started out one day to visit Napoleon on an Italian battle-
field when he had met another majesty, Death. But why
talk about it now? "At one time I received a handwritten
letter from His Majesty, in which he informed me that he
was very much in favor of the intentions of the Convention of Geneva, and approved all efforts toward their re-
alization."

"That's reason enough to put him here, in the middle,"
Reni decided.

The next stamp Reni found bore the head of King Johann of Saxony. He put that envelope next to the one from
Prussia because King Johann had received Henri Dunant
in Dresden.

"It was October 11th, 1863," Monsieur told the boy,
"when a carriage drawn by four horses called at my hotel
to take me to an audience with the king. When we arrived at the gate an old servant took me to the field marshal, who led me through part of the castle, to a small simple room. Before the field marshal left me, he explained
that the king would enter at the door across from where I
stood. I was to make three bows and wait for the king to
address me. The king arrived and I did as I had been told.
The king asked me, very kindly, what I wished. I explained
my mission and closed by saying: 'I would be deeply
grateful to Your Majesty if this project could be found

worthy of your protection and if you would send a representative to the congress which is about to be held in Geneva.' The King smiled and ended the audience by saying,
'I will do everything in my power, for a people who refuse
to participate in such humanitarian work would earn the
contempt of all mankind.' "

"That sounds like a fairy tale." Reni's eyes had become
bright with excitement. "Did he send a representative to
Geneva?"

"Yes, a representative from Saxony was present when
the congress began."

"Like a fairy tale," the boy repeated.

"Life is much like a fairy tale," Monsieur Dunant said.
In his heart he had kept a childlike faith that kind, noble
people were everywhere, friendly kings ruled their sub-
jects wisely, good deeds were rewarded and wicked men
were punished.

Reni had discovered a new ruler among the stamps.
"Who is this?" he asked.

"That is Emperor Franz Joseph, of Austria."

"Have you ever spoken to him?" Reni expected Monsieur Dunant to say that he had seen and spoken with this
monarch too, but the answer was no.

"When I went to Vienna, to see the Emperor, His Majesty was in Ischl, hunting. But I spoke to an archduke, Archduke Rainer."

"And what did the archduke say?"

"He condescended, in a very pleasant and kind manner,
to repeat three times, 'What a wonderful idea!' "

Reni was just as pleased by this reaction as Dunant, in his simplicity, had been at the time. The boy took the sentence as a promise for cooperation, as had Henri Dunant, and therefore asked confidently: "Did the Emperor of Austria then send a representative to Geneva?"

"No, the Emperor of Austria did not!"

"Well, we will put him alone for that; let him stand over there and be ashamed of himself," Reni said, putting the envelope to the left.

"I am certain he will soon recognize the great value of the resolution of Geneva," said Monsieur. He could not imagine anyone refusing to accept his idea. "I am positive that he will soon join the agreement. He is not the only one who would not accept my invitation. King Max of Bavaria and the Vatican have not yet sent representatives either."

"I have a new idea!" Reni announced. "Let's put the rulers who sent a representative to Geneva here, and the others over there."

The letters were looked through once more. Reni separated those rulers and governments that had signed the document on August 22nd from those that had not. Letters from countries that had not yet made up their minds were put in between.

When they were finished, there was quite a respectable number of letters at the right side of the desk, a much smaller number in the middle, and only a few at the left.

"But we still don't know what the letters say," said Reni. Monsieur Dunant showed no curiosity.

"I shall read them later on."

"Aren't you anxious to know what's in them?"

"No."

"Not the least bit?" Reni could not understand Monsieur's unconcern. If he had received a letter, even one, he would read it then and there; and these letters came from all over Europe.

"I think I know what's in them, at least in most of them . . . congratulations on my birthday."

Reni started, and remembered the little package. He blushed and held it out to Monsieur.

"Some more mail?"

"Yes," said Reni. There were no stamps on the package, and no return address. Monsieur could feel a small flat box through the wrapping.

"Where do you think this has come from?" he asked.

"I think it's from Switzerland," Reni stated importantly.

"From Switzerland . . . Why do you think so?"

"Well, I imagine . . . But you have to open it, like the letters."

Monsieur cut the string and unwrapped the package. He had been right; it contained a small box.

"If only I knew who it was from," said Monsieur, shaking his head.

"It comes from Geneva," Reni whispered. "You should open the box."

Monsieur Dunant lifted the cover of the little box. Carefully embedded in tissue paper was something that looked like a piece of material and a little stick. He took it out and saw that it was a small flag, with a red cross sewn coarsely on a piece of white linen.

"Ah, the Red Cross," said Monsieur in seeming surprise. The emblem of the red cross on a white cloth had been adopted by all the governments who had joined the Convention of Geneva to give protection to the medical personnel.

"It's just the opposite of the Swiss flag," Reni said, "I wonder why?"

"The colors were chosen out of gratitude to Switzerland, the country where the International Committee originated."

Reni wanted something to do with the flag, so he asked, "Where are we going to put the flag?"

"Let's put it on the shelf overlooking the kings on the stamps," suggested Monsieur Dunant.

"But it can't stand up."

Monsieur put it in an empty ink bottle so that it could stand erect, and placed it on the shelf over his desk. The flag waved proudly down on the monarchs.

"That's the way it should be," Monsieur said. "The idea of the Red Cross is international; the idea of brotherly help should be put above all national interests. All countries will realize that some day, they will all accept the demands of the Convention of Geneva . . ."

" . . . and they will want to stand on the right side!" Reni finished the sentence, threatening those rulers whose stamp-pictures were still standing on the left-hand side.

Just then a resounding tone could be heard from the hall.

"What's that?" Reni asked.

"That is the dinner gong, calling all the members of the family to the dining room."

Reni was disappointed that his visit had to end. "Do you have to go right away?" he asked.

"Yes, for today is my birthday."

"What are you going to get? Do you know?"

"Yes, I know. Thirty-seven roses!"

Reni and Monsieur Dunant walked downstairs together. When they reached the bottom, Reni shook hands with Monsieur and started out the door. Turning around, he called to Monsieur, "The flag is from me, for your birthday!"

CHAPTER SEVEN

1867

Paris had invited the world to its World's Fair in 1867, and the world had come, to see and to be seen. Crowds of people, Englishmen, Russians, Germans, Italians, Indians, all pushed one another from one pavilion to the next on the "Champs de Mars." Everyone was eager to see the many new inventions: here was a daring steel apparatus, a crane, which was strong enough to lift a wooden house off the ground; there was a steam plough which could plough across a field in hardly any time at all and without the help of an animal. The most exciting modern device was a telephone. It was possible to talk, through long wires, from one pavilion to another. The connection was not very clear and the voice sounded rather fuzzy, but the important part was that a conversation could be held. One could talk and listen through wires! One could telephone!

One of the gayest looking tents was that of the Red Cross, which had its own flag waving from the top of the tent as well as the flags of all the countries participating in the organization. The names of the five men who had formed its first board were engraved in golden letters on a white marble slab: Gustave Moynier, General Defour, Dr. Appia, Dr. Maunoir and Henri Dunant. In front of the tent there was also a white alabaster bust of Henri Dunant, crowned with a wreath of gilded laurels and identified by his name and birthdate on a black slate. What most people did not know was that Henri Dunant had been declared bankrupt in Geneva in 1866 and had fled the city, unable to pay his debts. Since that time the Geneva Committee of the Red Cross had been operating without him.

The exciting part of the Red Cross exhibit was inside the tent. Here the crowds could see plaster figures carefully made up to resemble wounded soldiers, with spots of red paint suggesting trickling blood, and supposedly wounded limbs completely bandaged. The figures seemed so lifelike that it took careful observation to realize that they were only plaster. The man with the injured head looked particularly real, and he received the loudest praise from the visitors. He sat on a litter and his head, bandaged crossways, was supported by nurses, also made of plaster.

"Well, that fellow would surely be dead now, if he really had such a wound," a stout man with a red face commented. "An injury like that one is very dangerous," he continued, proud of his statement. "I found that out a year ago in the war against the Austrians. Extremely dangerous!" he repeated, speaking German.

One of the two gentlemen from Geneva who were representing the Red Cross at the Exhibition answered him immediately, also in German. "You are mistaken, sir," he said. "Yes, he would die, if there was no Red Cross. But now he will not. You see, gentlemen, supposing he had been found on the battlefield by a male nurse of the Red Cross, he would have been bandaged up immediately. Then he would be carried on a stretcher to the Red Cross Station, where a doctor would do the necessary operation. Step up here, please," he said, pointing to the rear of the tent, "and you can see one of the Red Cross doctors performing the difficult surgery." There indeed was a plaster man, with a beard of white cotton, bending over a table of glossy white metal, holding a shiny scalpel between the plaster fingers of his right hand. A lean man in a long, white nightgown, eyes closed, could be seen on the operating table. Two nurses were standing next to him, holding a chloroform mask in their hands.

"Twelve, thirteen, fourteen, fifteen," a little redhaired girl counted aloud. She stood close to the velvet rope that separated the crowd from the exhibit. "Mother, there are fifteen figures," the child cried.

Suddenly a distinguished looking old gentleman addressed the two men from Geneva. "Is Monsieur Dunant in Paris?" he asked. Neither of the two attendants seemed to have heard the question, because they did not answer. One of them began to count the leaflets he held in his hands, while the other walked slowly to the rear of the tent and, taking a piece of muslin out of a show case, wiped dust off the faces of the plaster figures. The steam plough operating in the field next to the tent raised up a lot of dirt. He then walked over to the bust of Henri Dunant, and carefully dusted it, too.

"Can't you see he is here," the stout German said with a grin, "he is just getting his face cleaned."

But the man who had put the question paid no attention to him, and when the Red Cross attendant finished his job he introduced himself.

"Pardon me, my name is Jacques Boucard," he said, and then repeated his question, "Is Monsieur Dunant in Paris?"

This time the question could not very well be ignored, so the attendant came closer to the rope and said in a very subdued voice, "I am sorry, Monsieur, we don't know."

"You don't know?" Monsieur Boucard was somewhat surprised at this information.

"No."

The second man joined his colleague and added, "You know, Monsieur, that Monsieur Dunant left Geneva after he was found guilty of insolvency by the commercial court of our city. He is bankrupt and unfortunately can't even satisfy the most urgent claims of his creditors."

"How can that be possible?"

Both men shrugged their shoulders and began to speak at the same moment, until one granted priority to the other.

"The African projects of Monsieur Dunant turned out to be fatal blunders — you might even say mirages, caused by the heat!" The two men grinned. In their formal black clothes and black hats they looked like a pair of undertakers.

The visitors who stood near the tent drew closer to the three men. This was sensational! Dunant bankrupt! Remarks began flying around. Gamblers, that's what happens when you can't get enough! Another one, wouldn't you know! There was no voice of compasssion until Monsieur Boucard said,

"Someone ought to look after him. Maybe . . ."

"Maybe he committed suicide," a lady dressed in purple called out. "That's what usually happens to bankrupts."

Many of the onlookers joined in the conversation, agreeing that sometimes bankrupts did indeed commit suicide and that it was a shame not to know where Monsieur Dunant lived so that someone could look after him.

"But ladies and gentlemen, we do look after him," one of the two attendants protested. He pointed to the bust of Dunant, crowned with laurels. "We are looking after his better self, after the immortal Dunant! Nobody will cheat him out of the high praise he deserves. I don't think there is another living man whose bust stands crowned with a golden wreath of laurels at this fair."

"Yes, you adorn his bust of plaster with a wreath, but you do not know where the living Dunant is. You glorify his memory, but you do not as much as move a hand to protect him from the poverty into which he has probably sunk." Monsieur Boucard was obviously outraged.

The second member of the committee, who had been quiet until this time, began to lecture Monsieur Boucard as if he were preaching from a pulpit:

"A man and his accomplishments are not identical, Monsieur, don't forget that. A man may be unworthy, but nevertheless chosen, in spite of his unworthiness, to fulfill a most worthy task. Christ says. . . "

"That is not my opinion," Monsieur Boucard interrupted. "But if you want to quote Christ, it is He who says, 'By their fruits ye shall know them!' To me, this seems to be the only fitting quotation. A man who initiates such work as this. . . "

But the second attendant was eager to impress his audience with a sentence he had prepared: "Let the man Dunant be buried beneath his laurels. It can only be good for him, for his work and for his fame."

"I do not agree with your opinon," said Monsieur Boucard. "I have written a letter for Monsieur Dunant in case I did not find him here. As you can see, it is his birthday today." He pointed to the black slate under the bust of Dunant. "May 8th, 1828", it read. "Would you kindly accept this letter and deliver it to Monsieur Dunant as soon as he gets in touch with you. I assume that he will return to his work eventually, after having overcome the first shock."

"Certainly," one of the two men answered obligingly. "It is his duty to return, since he still holds the position of secretary of the International Committee." They accepted Monsieur Boucard's letter and the hurriedly scribbled notes of congratulation handed to them by the ladies. The stout German drew a one thousand franc note from his wallet and gave it to them, saying, "A bankrupt first of all needs money, and then good wishes." Some of the other visitors also decided to give a donation.

"You put us to shame," said one of the attendants as he collected the envelopes and bills.

"You needn't feel ashamed. The money is not for you, but for Monsieur Dunant." So saying, the German nodded to those around him and disappeared in the crowd. Monsieur Boucard also left the exhibit, and the other visitors drifted away to be replaced by new crowds coming to admire the fifteen figures in the Red Cross tent.

The two men relaxed after the people who had inquired about Henri Dunant had left the tent. Throughout the morning they handed out leaflets, told visitors about the Red Cross, dusted the dirt from the plaster faces. The man with the injured head was still being helped by the two nurses, the blood was still trickling through the white bandages. By noon the crowds diminished and the two men pushed aside a plaster patient and sat exhausted on a stretcher in the shade of the tent. They suddenly realized that a man had raised the rope and slipped through.

He stood in front of them as if he had dropped from the sky.

They recognized him instantly. "Bonjour, Monsieur Dunant," they blurted out, too surprised to say anything else. None of the few visitors to the tent at this hour realized that the large eyes, the beard, the soft chin and the smile around the mouth were the same on the bust and on the new arrival. The head of the bust was topped with flowing curls, which Henri Dunant had never possessed, but which were supposed to suggest the fiery spirit of a genius. The facial expression expressed heroic determination. Henri Dunant, the man, felt none of these vigorous feelings, not now; he was only very tired.

The two officials expressed their congratulations respectfully, but without any warmth of feeling. They said that it was almost certain that the Gold Medal of the Exhibition would be bestowed on him. They said there had been considerable interest in the Red Cross; so much in fact, that they were quite exhausted from answering questions after only half a day.

Monsieur Dunant in turn told them that he had heard that the Austrian Emperor intended to visit the exhibition. He suggested that everything should be prepared for the Emperor to sign the "Geneva Convention" on this occasion. He said that he would obtain information about when the Emperor planned to come to the Red Cross tent, and that he would make all the arrangements himself and would plan to be there himself to lay the Convention before Franz Joseph.

They promised to pass his information on to Geneva, so that all necessary steps for this important event could be supervised from there.

The conversation stopped. Henri Dunant looked over at the white plaster figures. They have never been at Solferino, he thought; they are so spotless, so dainty; they even smell clean. He remembered the terrible stench of the sick and dying inside the little church, and how he had tried to deodorize the polluted air by distributing tobacco. One after another of his assistants had stumbled out of the church, unable to stand the smell, until he had been left alone to help the wounded men.

"Attractive dummies," Dunant said.

The two attendants had not followed his thoughts and did not understand this comment. They seemed pleased by the praise.

"We will report to Geneva that the dummies have received your approval."

"Yes, yes, report that. Report what you must to Geneva. Report that I don't look as well groomed as your wounded, not as healthy as your dying men. My suit does not look as clean as the uniforms of your nurses."

"Your suit shows spots, indeed," one man said.

"Ink spots," Monsieur Dunant answered. "I have tried to dye the worn spots of my coat with ink. But I didn't succeed very well. I don't know much about such things. I don't know much about anything! Only one thing I understand: how the soldiers could be helped—not the dummies here, but the real ones. And that is the only thing I am not permitted to do!"

"Monsieur, you have done your part," the other man answered, only now noticing the bitterness in Dunant's voice. "The work has grown too big to be guided by one man alone!"

With a scornful laugh, Monsieur Dunant turned to leave. Why should he stay? One of the men raised the rope to let him pass through. But Dunant turned once more to glance over the tent and his eyes rested on the piece of marble on which were engraved the five names of the founders of the Red Cross. Gustave Moynier, he read, and smiled bitterly. "You have had an ideal vision," Moynier had said when they saw each other for the first time. Now Moynier had roused his own city against him. He printed slanderous lies about Dunant in the *Journal de Genève,* which the people of Geneva read with satisfaction while they sipped their morning tea. General Defour's name came next, the kind old gentleman who could not get his opinion heard against that of the majority. Dr. Appia and Dr. Maunoir — both were afraid for their own positions and had not as much as stirred a hand to help him when he had exiled himself from Geneva and fled to Paris. Neither of them had even bade him farewell. Poverty was a sin, at least in Geneva.

Dunant noticed the bust of himself with its laurel wreath for the first time. He stopped for a second, as if he wished to say something. But he remained silent, and, passing underneath the raised rope, he left the tent.

The two men breathed a sigh of relief when he left. One of them took the recently donated letters and bills out of his coat pocket and put them into a box which stood on a small table at the rear of the tent. He had been conscious of the pressure of them throughout the conversation, but what else could he do? Order were orders, and they had been told not to communicate anything to Dunant that had not been cleared with headquarters in Geneva.

The short lunch period was over, and the paths between the pavilions became filled with people again. Monsieur Dunant had not gone far when an extra large crowd drew his attention to an exhibit which had been put up almost opposite the Red Cross tent. It displayed the products of the firm of "Friedrich Krupp, Essen" — cannons!

A gun of shining metal was displayed on a foundation richly decorated with branches of pine. The barrel glistened and shone in the sun, and the black muzzle of the gun stared blankly at the visitors.

"These are the cannons of Sadowa," said a voice from the crowd.

"No wonder the Prussians could beat the Austrians."

The lady in the purple dress was among the onlookers. "Heavens, are they that clean?" she said. "They look very well cared for."

"Yes, we can be very proud of them. First quality! The name of Krupp is a recommendation in itself." The fat German who had given one thousand francs for the bankrupt Dunant was speaking. He patted the barrel with his hand proudly. "Perfectly clean; you are right, Madame. You can touch it with your silk gloves without getting them dirty. No scratch, not a speck of dust, no grease spot here." He spoke excitedly as if the cannons were his own, while actually his only connection with them was their mutual German nationality.

"Yes, shining outside, but pitch-black inside," was suddenly heard from a trembling voice. The visitors turned around to see a man in a worn coat with a drawn and tired face. He spoke German with an accent. "Open the lock and you will see the soul of such a beautiful body. All dirty, greasy, black. Puh!"

More and more visitors heard the conversation and pushed closer.

"Monsieur, don't you understand anything about weapons?" the German asked. "Naturally they need grease so that everything may move smoothly. There must not be any resistance."

"Everything smooth, no resistance!" Henri Dunant repeated as his excitement grew, for it was he who was becoming so agitated. "Open the lock, open the lock," he demanded until the representative of the firm of Krupp stepped forward and did open the lock. A shiny sliding-carriage popped out, and in its grooves was a thick greenish grease to enable it to glide more smoothly.

"The shell is put in on top of this," the Krupp man explained in a loud voice to distract the visitors from the strange words of the man who kept interrupting him.

"That is the soul, the greasy soul!"

"What is all that about the soul," cried the German, exasperated at the turn of the conversation. "This is precision work. It is for this that we expect to get the Gold Medal."

"The Gold Medal?" His questioner was obviously stunned.

The Krupp official considered his silence a sign of speechless admiration and he repeated proudly, "Yes, Monsieur! It is for this that we expect the Gold Medal, the first prize of the Paris World's Fair."

Henri Dunant felt dizzy. Where was he? What kind of a world was this? In the hot afternoon he heard the buzzing of voices and the noise of the steam plough. Laughing people floated above his head in little cars of the suspension railway, waving at him. And here in front of him was a machine built to extinguish man, a cannon, whose inventors were to be presented with the same gold medal that he, as founder of the Red Cross and opponent of these same weapons, was due to receive. Tears gathered in his eyes and rolled down his cheeks. He hurried away, scarcely seeing where he was going.

"A crackpot," the German said scornfully, "un fou!" and everyone around him laughed and moved on to another exhibit.

Henri Dunant plunged back into the Red Cross tent, furious that the same crowds who had admired the Red Cross figures could admire a cannon. He climbed over the rope barrier and rushed up to the bust of himself.

"I don't want any laurels," he stammered, and he tried

to tear the gilded wreath from the alabaster head. "Take it down!"

When the two attendants hurried over, he made an effort to control his voice, saying: "Gentlemen, take this wreath off my bust. I don't want it. I don't want a gold medal either, a gold medal which a munitions maker will also receive!"

The two men were so confused that they obeyed immediately. One of them removed the torn wreath from the bust, while the other one led the sobbing man into the rear of the tent where people could not see him. He pushed Dunant towards an empty stretcher and returned to the entrance of the tent to help his colleague distribute leaflets containing the articles of the Convention of Geneva.

Henri Dunant sat on the stretcher, his head in his hands, asking himself over and over, "What kind of a world is this?" He looked into the faces of the plaster figures, but they stared back at him blankly, unable to answer his need for human companionship.

After a while the attendants thought that the witnesses of the scene had moved on, and one of them gave the other a sign. The one who had led Dunant into the rear of the tent went back to him and, lifting the canvas corner of the tent, pushed him out without even saying good-bye.

"It will be better if you do not come back, Monsieur," he said when Dunant attempted to speak. "Better for your work," he continued, trying to excuse his harsh manner, "whose devoted servants we are."

Dunant stood still a moment, dazed by the bright sunshine. Then he started walking through the Fair grounds, looking at the faces of the people who passed him. He left the Fair and wandered through the streets of the city; it seemed to him that everywhere he looked he saw abundance. Fruit stands, flower markets, windows filled with meat and cheese, poultry and fish, he saw them all as if in a dream. In the baker's shop he looked at long sticks of white bread and his imagination recalled the smell of freshly baked bread so vividly that he ached. Everywhere he looked food was plentiful, and yet there were people who were hungry and in need. He knew it now, for he was one of them.

He came to the Rue de Neuilly and climbed the stairs to the attic room which was all that he could now afford. He walked over to his tiny window and gazed out at the evening sky, now turning a delicate pink and tinting, with a soft and indescribable beauty, the gray roofs of the city.

What kind of a world was this?

CHAPTER EIGHT

1871

Paris was preparing for civil war. The workers had rebelled against the government, spurred into protest by France's humiliating defeat in the Franco-Prussian War of 1870. Now the workers fought at barricades set up in the streets against the soldiers of General Thiers, who used brutal methods in an attempt to halt the fighting before it turned into full-scale revolution.

For most of the citizens of Paris, those who were not involved on either side, the fighting was frightening and horrible. In the little restaurant of the Gare du Nord, only a few tables were occupied, and these by people who felt safer there than at home. They hid their faces behind the pages of their newspapers, smoking innumerable cigarettes and drinking one cup of coffee after another. Few of these people were in the station restaurant because they were travelers, although any one of them would have liked to travel as far as possible away from Paris. Their longing to get away had brought them to the station, but most of them could not get permission to leave.

Paris was not safe, and the coffee-drinkers at the restaurant were well aware of it. Spring had brought bullets instead of swallows this year, and they came flying from Versailles, where the troops were stationed. If one was unlucky, the pavement in front of one's feet would be torn up by shrapnel, or a wall would come crumbling down and its bricks flying. Besides these obvious dangers, the city was full of spies and informers who reported to the government all those who seemed suspicious, who were in the way, or against whom the informers felt spiteful. A word to the officials, twelve bullets for the victim, and a handful of paper money to the informer!

By the window of the station restaurant, a tall gentleman with gray hair shook his head over his newspaper. It was the *Moniteur* of May 8th, 1871, which described the preparations for a dreadful street battle expected any day. "Paris today is filled with dynamite and explosives, with bombs and mines. One fire is bound to kindle the next ...." The *Moniteur* put its readers' fears in black and white, and the same thing could be read in the other papers. War! The gray-haired gentleman, who had been

looking anxiously out of the window at too-frequent intervals, looked out once again, then nervously checked his
watch.

This gentleman, Monsieur Lefebre, was the owner of
a small watch-repair and jewelry shop in the Rue LaFayette. His business had been damaged by conditions in the
city, and all he wanted was to leave. But how could he
leave? No trains were running except a short one which
departed a few times a day, from the Gare du Nord to St.
Denis. But no one was allowed to board it unless he could
show a special permit issued by the Central Committee,
or could prove to be the owner of a foreign passport.
Who was lucky enough to get such a permit, or better still,
to own a foreign passport? By no means the agitated Monsieur Lefebre.

All that the jeweler owned in the world was his stock
of watches, which he carried with him in a suitcase. He
had packed in such a hurry that there had been no time to
stop them, so that a lively ticking could be heard from under the table. In spite of the layers of cotton wrapping,
the watches ticked away and the suitcase gave off a sound
like the scratching of some strange insect carrying a heavy
body on many tiny legs.

Monsieur Lefebre took another look out of the window,
but there was no sign of the man he was waiting for. If
the man did not come, the watchmaker was lost. He would
not pass by unnoticed a second time, carrying a suitcase
between Rue LaFayette and the station. If he had to make
that trip again, he might as well give away his treasures

in the station, except that nobody would want them. It was dangerous to own anything, these days.

The St. Denis train was just being assembled on the first track. In a few minutes, it would be on its way to safety. Safety, for himself and his watches, was all Monsieur Lefebre dreamed of. It seemed to him that the ticking under the table was gaining speed, that the funny centipede in his suitcase had started to run faster. If the gentleman he was waiting for did not show up, the train would leave without him.

"Excuse me, Monsieur."

A young man stood in front of the table, but he was not the man expected. He took a seat without waiting for permission. The watchmaker did not pay much attention to him, but he noticed that he was young, that his hard face was clean-shaven and his suit cheap but clean. Perhaps he was a worker, or a young student.

The young man did not matter. What did matter was that the passport arrived. Could the whole arrangement be a fake? Monsieur Lefebre could not believe that Baron de la Tuque, who had set it all up, would have failed him. The Baron had promised that the Swiss gentleman would call for him in this place, just before train time, to give him the passport and his ticket, paid in advance. The Swiss had done this before and was supposed to be reliable.

The young man was eying him oddly, so Monsieur Lefebre took up his newspaper once more. Did he hear the watches? The ticking seemed to have grown much louder; no longer the scratching of little feet, it sounded like the pounding of heavy shoes — bang, bang, bang! The watchmaker tapped on the floor with his own foot, to disguise the sound. He looked over his paper at the young man, who was reading his own paper, an English *Daily Telegraph.* That seemed odd and suspicious to Monsieur Lefebre, who was nervous enough to find informers everywhere. The young man lowered his paper, too; the men's eyes met, and they both felt guilty. They had to say something, anything, to cover up their mutual suspicion.

"Who is this Monsieur Dunant?" asked the young man.

Good Heavens! Is he a mind reader? I am trapped! thought Lefebre. I am sitting opposite a spy; he knows everything.

A question had been asked; he must answer. His lips were quivering, his mouth dry, as he said:

"I don't know. I don't know anyone named Dunant."

Admiring his own nerve, he went on: "Why do you ask?" He stopped his silly pounding on the floor, feeling suddenly relaxed.

"I just read about him in the *Daily Telegraph*," the fellow said.

He must be a student after all, the watchmaker figured, or he wouldn't be reading an English paper.

"What do the English write about him?"

"The Paris correspondent of the *Telegraph* writes . . ." The young man picked up his paper again. Finding the article, he translated it fluently, keeping his voice subdued:

" . . . Henri Dunant, the originator of the Geneva Con-

vention and its different auxiliaries, is present in the
French capital in order to save women, children and the
needy of Paris from the terror of an approaching confla-
gration in this enormous city, which is bound to follow either the bombing by the government or the measures of the
Commune, which is tearing up whole steets in prepara-
tion for its defense. Monsieur Dunant holds a position between the parties, and has, in this position, the means ..."

The translation was interrupted by Monsieur Lefebre's
sudden turn towards the entrance. A man of about fifty
years of age had come into the restaurant. He was looking
around him. The watchmaker quickly bent down for his
suitcase and pulled it from under the table. In the meantime, the stranger had seen him and was approaching the
table in the window.

"Bon soir, Messieurs," he said, with a friendly bow. Ad-
dressing the watchmaker, he continued, without lowering
his voice: "Here, Monsieur Lefebre, is the passport. The
ticket is in it." Taking a brown leather folder from his
pocket, he put it down on the table. Before Lefebre covered
it with his hand, the young man saw that it was a light-
colored leather folder, stamped with the Swiss coat-of-arms.
The watchmaker shook hands with the man who had
given him the passport, nodded to the student, and reached
for his suitcase. As he left, the newcomer called after
him, "And don't forget ... "

Had the watchmaker not called back, "I know, I know,"
the trusting Swiss would have given away the secret of
how the passport was to be returned to him. As it was, he

signalled that he would wait in the restaurant. He sat down on the chair vacated by Monsieur Lefebre.

A waiter came to take the new guest's order. He hesitated.

"A cup of black coffee; a small one, please."

"May I buy you a drink, Monsieur?" the student asked.

"No, thank you. I don't drink any alcohol."

"Can I order anything else for you?"

The gentleman smiled. "That's very kind of you. A glass of milk, perhaps, if you don't mind."

"A large glass of milk for the gentleman, and a cognac for me," he ordered. The waiter left.

The man in Lefebre's chair wiped his forehead. He must have been running, for he looked exhausted. He looked worn out, old, and unkempt, the student thought. He gave him a closer look and realized that his suit, which must have been black originally, now had big purple stains on it. Once, perhaps, his collar had been white, and his beard combed, but it was hard to tell. In spite of all this, there was something about the old man that stopped his companion from summing him up with the phrase: poor devil.

Obviously he was Swiss, and obviously he lent out his passport and a middle man returned it after the escape. It infuriated the student that people exist — in every generation — who profit by the misfortunes of their fellow men, without any effort on their own part. In this case, it was through the good luck of owning a passport that could be lent to others for a fee. Why should a man receive money just because he was born in a country like Switzerland, which was spared the horrors of war? Probably, the student thought, this man is hiding his profits behind a mask of poverty. I might not resent him so much if he used his profit for his own person, for decent clothes, for food! But here he has even accepted a glass of milk from me, and he looks like a tramp while he makes a fortune on his passport! What a crook he is, and what a coward!

Still, he thought, there is something about him that makes me wonder if I am right. Perhaps I am being deluded by his childish request for a glass of milk; or perhaps it is his smile, his naive expression. The student was puzzled.

"Are you a foreigner?" he finally asked, in a friendlier tone than he had intended.

"Yes."

The waiter came back with the order. The glass of milk was more expensive than the cognac. In wartime, milk was rare, its transportation difficult. The old man felt embarrassed as he noticed the price, and he apologized:

"I wouldn't have ordered a glass of milk, if I had known. I only thought . . . I haven't had anything today. . . . "

The student looked at him. Could that be true? He must have made at least ten thousand francs just now. Why did he try to give this impression of poverty?

The boy raised his glass. "To your health! My name is Léon."

"My name is Henri," his companion said, raising his

own glass. Léon emptied his drink and asked, unex-
pectedly:

"How much does your passport cost?"

"My passport?"

"Yes."

"Nothing. The government issues one to every citizen
who applies for it."

The student bit his lips. Why does he play so dumb?
He must be suspicious of me.

"I happened to see that you gave your passport to the
man who sat here, just before . . ."

"I thought . . ." Henri's face was frightened.

"You thought I was his friend."

"Yes."

"I didn't know him at all."

"His name is Monsieur Lefebre, a watchmaker in the
Rue LaFayette. He has a sick mother in St. Denis. He
wants to help her, to take some food to her. She has nobody
to take care of her."

"He was taking a suitcase full of contraband, of goods
which should be the property of all the people."

"He has a sick mother in St. Denis; don't you understand?" The old man seemed helpless. He repeated to the
student the words of Baron de la Tuque: "Monsieur Lefebre has a sick mother in St. Denis. It is an act of charity
to help a son to get to his mother."

"How much does he pay for it?"

"He does not pay anything for it."

It's impossible to get anything out of him, thought the

boy. I guess he doesn't think I'm serious about "renting" his passport.

"Garçon — another cognac, and a glass of milk!"

After he had been served, the student repeated his question. "How much does he pay for it?"

"He does not pay anything." Henri was almost amused at the investigation. The thought of smuggling human beings for money made him smile.

The boy half closed his eyes. "I can make you tell the truth," he whispered.

"And I can't tell you anything but the truth, and I have done that already."

Monsieur Léon reached into his pocket and took a red card from a black leather wallet.

"My identification — National Guard!"

He smiled, but it was a bitter smile. "I could have you arrested this very minute for helping a fugitive, for suspicion of espionage, for your aid in smuggling property."

The old man understood. He suddenly realized that the young man was no longer playing a game which could be stopped at any time. This was reality. He was really sitting in this smoky restaurant, at a dirty table with two glasses on it. Across from him, there really was a hard young face and an outstretched hand holding the credentials of the National Guard.

Resigning himself to reality, he asked: "What do you want from me?"

Léon was silent. He could now demand anything. He could take away every penny the old miser had made with his passport. What he wanted more, however, was his freedom. Paris was too dangerous. True, he was listed with the National Guard, but for how much longer? Already he had been denounced as a spy by someone who hated him, and he had better get out of town before he got into real trouble.

"I want your passport."

"I don't have it with me," Henri answered.

"I know. But you will get it back; that's what you are waiting for."

Monsieur Dunant became frightened. "I will tell you the truth," he said. "An inspector will bring it back. But he is innocent. He keeps the passport when the inspection is over, and he always brings it back to me."

"So, you admit you have helped people before?"

"I do." The old man would not have denied it in any case. "I've helped some people to flee from Paris because it was the only way for them to escape death, and because I do not think their deaths would have been just. They had done nothing except hold different political opinions from the men in power. I did not help them for money, but because I do not think it is right to persecute a man because of his opinions."

He talked on feverishly, but his thoughts went around in circles. Without a passport, I am ruined; without a passport, I am nobody, I have entry nowhere, I can never again help anyone; and that's the worst of all.

At last the student came close to the truth, realizing that Henri was a fanatic who was taken advantage of by others.

"I think your passport is coming back," he said.

An inspector stood at the door, dressed in the blue suit and black hat of the railroad personnel. He walked toward the table, and Dunant wondered — but too late — if there was anything he could do to prevent the return of the passport.

The inspector saluted and put the document on the table. "Everything is all right, Monsieur," he said. "You should not get so excited every time. You can depend on me."

The old man tried to smile, and the official nodded and went away. On the marble table between the two man lay a brown leather folder, engraved in gold. It was the passport of a peaceful citizen of a foreign country, but the red card in Léon's pocket was stronger still, and its owner was the more powerful of the two men.

Monsieur Dunant looked sad, and pushed the priceless document across the table. His hand shook as it touched the black marble.

The young man opened the passport, and read the first page. Almost immediately, he dropped the document and stared at his companion.

"Henri Dunant?"

The old man rose, as if in court, and answered clearly: "Yes."

"Swiss citizen?"

"Swiss citizen!"

"Born May 8th, 1828?"

"Right."

Somewhat embarrassed, the young man stood up, too. "Monsieur Dunant, how can I return your passport?"

" . . . Return it?"

"Yes, I only need it to get out of Paris."

Dunant held onto the table. "Why didn't you say so?"

"It's hard to tell the truth nowadays."

The old man smiled softly. "Poor boy. I will wait here. Take the train to St. Denis, and after the inspection, hand the passport to the man in uniform you saw here."

Léon put the document into his pocket and buttoned up his coat.

"You can easily get a ticket with the passport; nobody will look at it too closely," said Dunant.

The young man took a five hundred franc note from his wallet, and pushed it over to the other man.

"Do you still believe I take money for it?"

"I don't, I don't, but — I want you to buy yourself another glass of milk."

But Dunant refused the money. "Keep it. You will need it. Life is no cheaper outside of Paris."

Léon put the money back. He almost wanted to stay with this old man, who reminded him of his own father, even though he knew no more about him than he had learned from the correspondent of the *Daily Telegraph*: "Monsieur Dunant stands between the parties . . ."

"Au revoir, Monsieur."

"Au revoir."

They shook hands. Then the boy left the restaurant.

I hope he made the train, thought Monsieur Dunant.

Again he sat back in his corner and waited for the passport.

When the waiter came around and asked for his order, he stopped to think for a moment before answering:

"A cup of black coffee — a small one, please."

CHAPTER NINE

1878

The countryside of the Tessin slept underneath a starry sky. Silver threads wove a pattern in the glittering sky. The night was round and smooth, interrupted only by the sharp mountain peaks around its edges.

Although no air was stirring, the waves of the lake crept up the white, pebbled beach, whispering to the stones. Playfully, they rocked the fishing boats anchored in the lake. Briskly they splashed the sides of the boats, pulling them toward the shore. On their return, they tugged at the boats to follow out into the lake, until the vessels' short chains stopped them. The boats pulled and strained at their chains when the waves came, then settled back to bob peacefully until the next waves rolled in.

One of the boats hardly moved at all. Swaying gently, it stayed behind when the others tried to escape from their chains.

In this boat lay an old man.

He had leaned two oars against the back seat and had stretched out on them, as on a bed, staring up at the sky. He had to change his position now and then, for the oars were hard. Other things, during the past two years, had been harder still. Here, at least, he was alone. He had often been lonely lately, but almost never alone. Around noon, at some convent door or other refuge for the poor, a line of ragged creatures, tin cups in hand, was usually ahead of him. In the evening, if he took shelter in some smoky station waiting room, most of the benches would be occupied when he arrived. Often he had to sit on the floor, crouched in between other vagrants, if he wanted a roof over his head for the night. For a time, he had been sure that he would never be able to sleep in such surroundings: the woman next to him snoring, mouth wide open; the old fellow on the other side breathing out clouds of alcohol; a child crying. In the beginning, he had to rush outside to escape from the crowds of poor people whom he hated. When he was young, he visited and cared for the poor according to the commands of charity; but in those days he could escape when the day was done. He could go home, wash, change his clothes, and make notes on the "cases" he had helped that day. Now he was forced to share everything with the poor, even the polluted, sweaty air.

As time went on, he grew accustomed to it, and his hatred diminished. But his compassion did not return. He had come to believe that there was no way to help the poor — not with gifts or kindness, certainly not with sermons. Poverty was a plague; it had taken hold of the bodies and souls of the poor, and there was no cure. Many times he had seen a beggar receive a large gift of money and had seen, too, that in just a few hours the money was gone. The cancer of poverty consumed it at once.

Had he behaved differently? Could he be helped?

The boat was swaying gently, rocking away like an old-fashioned cradle. Did I ever rest in a cradle? Dunant wondered. Yes, most likely, most certainly. It is fifty years today since I first lay in a cradle. Fifty years ago I was asleep in a cradle trimmed with lace, covered with a down quilt. Today I am trying to sleep in this boat, covered with nothing.

He could not fall asleep, though he had walked miles since morning. The pain in his stomach was too annoying to let him rest. He was hungry. He could feel, right through the cloth of his pocket, a hard roll he had bought that evening. But the roll was for the next morning, for his birthday breakfast. His hand slipped into his pocket and pulled out the crumbs that had flaked off the crust.

Determined to wait till morning for the roll, he nibbled the few crumbs. To his starved senses they brought back the fragrance of the bakery, and for a moment he believed himself back in the shop. He reached out his arm toward the imaginary loaves of bread, and his movement caused the boat to tilt slightly, bringing a rush of cold water over the side.

The old man woke up from his half-dream abruptly and came back to reality. Reality meant that he was lying in a fishing boat on May 8th, 1878. He was without a single coin and did not know whether he was in Italy or across the border, in Switzerland. Reality meant that he had one roll, which he was determined to keep until dawn.

Why had he made that resolution? What use was sentiment, when hunger was eating away his courage? He started to pull the roll from his pocket when a new and frightening thought restrained him:

Why torment yourself at all? Why drag on this worn-out, hungry existence? Is not half a century a long enough life? Why not die, and shake off the misery, hunger, fatigue, and poverty? Why not?

The waves showed him how. If he rolled to one side of the boat, it would tilt enough to let the water come in. It would fill up the boat slowly, then send it to the bottom, turning it into a watery cradle. He did not fear death; he could afford to share his roll with the fish.

If he really wanted to die, he must pray. But he had forgotten how to pray during the hard years just past. He had not defied God, nor doubted Him, but weariness had replaced prayer as it had replaced almost everything else.

Why worry? If he could only relax, drift, give in to his

weariness, surely the boat would do the rest. But the boat resisted each time he rocked it below the water level, and the old man knew that something in him was protecting himself. A boat cannot resist by itself. Try it again, slowly; take your time; try it again!

The water is so dark. Better not look into it. Look up to the stars, look up; that's better. Move to the side. The water was coming into the boat now, and one hand was already in the water.

What was that? The stars glittered, seeming to move all over the sky. They were dancing in circles. Was it the stars, or was it lights from across the lake? They were shaking! There, one tore loose from the rest. It was gliding over the surface of the lake. It was coming for him — a star, an angel!

Shivering, the old man sat up in the boat, and the vessel steadied itself.

A boat was approaching, a lantern fastened to its stern. The old man could hear the oars beat, their sound breaking the stillness of the night. As the boat came nearer, he could make out two figures. The beam from their lantern now struck the empty boats, and soon it shone upon him.

"Who's there?" called one of the men.

The old man did not answer. He smiled. Not a star, a Swiss coast guard boat! Two customs officers — are they your angels, Lord?

He could see the two men now. The oarsman was very young, a surprised expression on his childish face. His fair hair had fallen over his forehead. The man who was standing was middle-aged; he was heavy and strong, with a dark mustache.

"Stand up! Put up your hands!" shouted the older man.

They talk like men, my angels, thought Dunant, and it made him smile again. He made an effort to get up, holding on to the sides of his boat, but he stepped on one of the oars. It splashed into the water. He tried to reach it, but the voice called again:

"Stay where you are!"

The lad in the coast guard boat fished the oar out of the water as he maneuvered his craft next to the fishing boat.

The old man stood upright, hands raised.

"Do you have any weapons?" asked the officer.

Dunant shook his head.

"You may drop your hands."

He dropped his hands and fell back on the bench.

"I didn't say you could sit down," snapped the dark man.

"I am very tired, lieutenant," said the old man, trying to get up again. The silver bars on the sleeve and shoulder of the officer's uniform revealed his rank.

"All right, stay put. What are you doing out here, in the middle of the night?"

"I wanted to sleep."

"That's no reason to be drifting in a boat, five hundred yards from the Swiss border."

"Don't we all drift about, awake or asleep?" asked Dunant. His voice was no longer frightened and shaky; it seemed to come from far away, as if from the bottom of the lake where he had seen himself, only moments ago, dead.

"Maybe you do, but I'm on duty! Are you a stranger here?"

"Yes, I am strange here."

"Who are you?"

"Who am I?" the old man said, and nodded. That was his own question: Who am I?

"Do you have any papers?"

How often had he heard this question, at all the borders in Europe. Reaching into his coat pocket, he pulled out a once-brown leather case, his Swiss passport, and handed it to the officer.

"Well, at least you have identification." The officer began to turn the pages, as hundreds of his colleagues had done before him. "They are even in order. You are a citizen of Switzerland. Can't you read, that you don't know who you are?"

The lieutenant laughed, glancing at his young partner and making a gesture that indicated that the old man was crazy. But the boy did not answer. He was looking at Dunant and thinking:

Your hair is white, and you still ask the question I ask myself. Who am I? Perhaps even my lieutenant had to ask himself that once, before he became so proud and self-assured.

The officer handed the papers back, and asked with a scornful smile:

"And where are you going now, Monsieur Dunant?"

As he heard himself addressed by name, some of his old spirit came back to Henri Dunant. His past came alive again. Yes, he was the famous Henri Dunant, even if the officer had never heard of him. He answered as he used to:

"I haven't decided. Perhaps to Paris or London. Maybe I'll go first to Germany, to Berlin or to Stuttgart. Or should I go east, to Vienna or Petersburg or Moscow?"

The names enchanted him. He could see the halls crowded with people who were waiting for his lectures; he could see the salons filled with people who longed to speak to him.

The simple Swiss customs officer was puzzled. The old man seemed to present a more complex problem than he had first thought.

"Do you know somebody in any of those places?" he asked.

"Of course!" Monsieur Dunant was his old self again. "I know the Duke of Fezensac in Paris, among others, and the Baron de la Tuque. I used to know His Majesty, the Emperor Napoleon III."

As he noticed the expression of doubt on the officer's face, Dunant took a printed card out of his pocket, a copy of a note. He handed it to the lieutenant, who read that His Majesty, Napoleon III, thanked Monsieur Dunant for his lasting friendship and expressed his congratulations on the inauguration of the International Court of Arbitration. The date was 1873, the place Brighton. It must have been written during the Emperor's exile in England.

While the officer read, Dunant continued his story, listing his important friends in the capitals of Europe. In London, he knew Secretary Morley, Lord Elcho, and the famous Florence Nightingale; in Stuttgart, Professor Mueller and Pastor Wagner; in Vienna, the Swiss ambassador and Archduke Rainer; in Berlin, Their Majesties. The celebrities of his former life passed by in a ghost parade, and he smiled. When the officer tried to return his card, he refused to take it.

"You keep it. I have a few more copies."

But the officer had no use for this souvenir. He returned the card of the ex-Emperor to the ragged man in the fishing boat and said to him: "Come over here." He did not dare to let drift on the lake a man who knew rulers of half of Europe — or claimed he did.

Monsieur Dunant stepped awkwardly into the coast guard boat. The young aide helped to settle him comfortably on one of the seats.

"Let's go!" ordered the lieutenant, and taking the lanern, he took his place in the stern.

The boat was pushed rapidly forward by the strong strokes of the oars. It made a white streak over the lake, the surface of which was now a leaden gray. Monsieur Dunant felt quite at ease. He crossed his legs and dragged one hand through the water. He watched the stars; they were quietly back in their places, quietly moving toward morning.

After a while, he reached into his pocket for his birthday roll. The boy smiled at him, pleased to see him so comfortable, and Dunant smiled back.

Life was a beautiful thing, after all. On his fiftieth birthday, he was being rowed across a lake, its surface a shield of silver.

Where to?

Did it make any difference? He was no longer afraid. Did it matter whether he went to London, Paris, Vienna or to an obscure little country jail, while the gentlemen made up their minds whether his freedom would endanger the safety of the country? Did any of it matter?

Monsieur Dunant ate his roll, and smiled.

CHAPTER TEN

1887

Heiden, a small town in the Swiss mountains of Appen-
zell, had just started to become popular as a resort. For-
eigners, mostly Germans, began arriving with the migra-
tory birds in the spring and leaving with them in the fall.
The next year they would be back, accompanied by the
friends to whom they had sung praises of this lovely vaca-
tion spot.

The people of Heiden were delighted with the popu-
larity of their village. At town meetings the mayor told
them that the tourists came to Heiden to escape from the
hustle and noise of the world; therefore, there must be

no loud entertainments and the children must learn to be quiet and polite. They built walks up to the hills surrounding the little town and supplied benches at convenient spots so that the tourists could stop and enjoy the view of Lake Konstanz. This lake, locally called the "Swabian Sea," would change during the day from a golden shade to a deep blue, depending on the hour and position of the sun. The people of Heiden quickly found that there was money in hospitality, and many turned their houses into inns or hotels.

One late spring day in 1887 Mr. Sonderegger, the schoolmaster of Heiden, came home for lunch after school. He sat down at the table and said to his wife, "Evidently there is an eccentric in Heiden who arrived last night."

The eight Sonderegger children sitting around the table became interested. Reinhard, the second youngest child, asked immediately, "Mama, what is an eccentric?"

The other children started to giggle and were reprimanded by their mother. Reinhard realized that he had become the center of attention, so he asked again,

"What is an eccentric?"

"You are not supposed to interrupt your father when he is speaking," his mother reminded him.

"The story I have heard is not very clear," Mr. Sonderegger continued. "The children told me this morning that they met a man in shabby clothes who smiled at them in a friendly manner. But he looked very strange and unusual; he had long white hair and a beard hanging down almost to his knees."

"That does sound strange indeed," said Mother. "Did any one of you see him?" she asked her children. But they all answered no.

"He must have been around the upper part of the village when school started," the father explained, "because the children who came from that direction saw him. They said they were not afraid of him, in spite of his queer looks. The children said that he looked like a prophet."

Reinhard saw a new opportunity to be the clown, so he quickly asked, "Mama, what is a prophet?" His sisters and brothers looked down at their plates. If they looked at each other, they knew they would laugh and Father would not stand for that.

Then the baby, Heini, who was sitting on his mother's lap, shouted gleefully, "A pophet, a pophet!" He could not say his R's yet, and this pronunciation caused the rest of the children to break into gales of laughter.

"That's enough, stop laughing!" said their mother sternly. "And you, Reinhard, you should be ashamed of yourself. You ought to know what a prophet is. You hear Father read out of the Bible every night. If you had paid attention, you would know."

"You tell him, Wilhelm," Father directed, and Wilhelm, who was Father's pet, got up, pushed back his plate and said:

"Prophets are wise men, who were told by God to tell people the truth which, in their blindness, they would not otherwise be able to recognize."

"That's right. You may sit down, Wilhelm." Father was

satisfied, but Reinhard was not. He wanted to ask what blindness meant, and what sort of truth the prophets had to tell the people, but he didn't dare. So he just sighed and said, more to himself than to the others:

"But the prophets are all dead, I thought."

His mother had heard his comment and said to him, "Our Lord can always send prophets again. You should know that, too, Reinhard."

"We do not know this man is a prophet; the children only said he looked like one," said Father.

"I think they only said that because they had never seen a man with a long white beard before," added Mother.

"That's right," Father agreed. "Now finish eating, so that you all grow to be big and strong someday."

After a short silence Reinhard spoke again. "Mama, I want to be a prophet someday."

This set the other children off again. The two oldest boys almost choked, they were laughing so hard, and they had to be excused from the room.

When Wilhelm and Oswald returned to the table, they heard their father say that if they spoke about the "prophet" once more, he would get really angry. Everyone tried very hard to be serious, but little innocent Heini made even the schoolteacher smile by singing, "Pophet, pophet," and all the children started giggling again.

Mother got up to take the dishes out and Emma, the oldest girl, collected the spoons. Mother must have been thinking about the eccentric, for when she returned from the kitchen she asked, "What is he doing here anyway?"

The schoolmaster did not know. "The children only told me that he was walking through the village slowly. He stopped often and looked at the houses. Those who had met him further out said that he would bend down from time to time to pick up a stone which he would hold up against the light, and then put in his pocket. Or he would bend down to smell a flower, but he would not pick it."

"Mama, do all prophets act like that?" asked Reinhard, trying hard to make the others laugh again. But this time it didn't work. They didn't feel like laughing any more. Reinhard was disappointed and he also felt rather embarrassed.

Suddenly Oswald, who was sitting next to the window, surprised everyone by saying, "There he is!"

For a moment the children hesitated, looking at their mother to see if she was going to get up to look at the man. When she rose from her seat, they jumped up, too, and dashed over to crowd around Oswald. Father was the last one to walk over.

"Yes that must be the man," Mr. Sonderegger said. "The description the children gave me fits him."

An old man was walking slowly down the village street in the hot noon sun. He was dressed in black, but he was too far away to tell what sort of clothes he had and whether he looked rich or poor. He wore nothing on his head and his face was framed by his loose, white hair. He seemed to be smiling, and his white beard really did come down to his knees.

"The children did not exaggerate," said Mother. The family stared, fascinated, at the strange figure walking down the street. The old man was not alone. He had his right hand on the shoulder of one of the boys of the village and was letting the boy guide him.

"That's Ferdi Spiess walking with him," Oswald whispered.

"Ferdi!" Reinhard cried through the window. The old man and the boy were directly below them now. Reinhard's sisters and brothers told him to be quiet.

"But Ferdi is my friend," he told the others. "He gave me a marble once." But no one was paying any attention to him, they were too busy peering out the window at the unusual pair. Ferdi did look up to the window, but he did not wave, he only nodded his head and looked straight ahead again. He was walking carefully, trying not to stir up too much dust with his bare feet and trying to avoid the stones. The old man looked closely at all the houses they passed.

"All right, let's finish eating," Father said, "or the table will be cleared before dessert."

"Oh no!" the children protested, and all ran back to the table. They were having cherry dumplings for dessert today and no one wanted to miss them, particularly because they were the first cherry dumplings of the year. There was a tradition that the person who had the most cherry pits left on their plate on the first day would be cherry king for the year. So the minute dessert was finished, the room was quiet while everyone counted their pits.

Before they finished, however, there was a knock on the door. Father called, "Come in."

Ferdi Spiess, the boy who had led the strange man down the street, walked into the room. The children jumped up. The cherry king and his attendant privileges were forgotten. Rushing to the door, the children crowded around their friend, each of them trying to find out first who the old man was, where he came from, and what he wanted here.

After Ferdi had greeted his teacher, he explained, "I don't know who he is. Dr. Altherr did not tell me where he came from or what he wanted in Heiden, but he did seem to recognize his name."

"How did you come to talk to him, and what has Dr. Altherr got to do with it?" Mr. Sonderegger asked.

The boy answered, "Well, it was this way. I ran across the square to the fountain, where the stranger was standing with the grocer, and I heard them talking."

"Does the grocer know the man?"

"No. I think the man only inquired about a room, so she recommended the 'Paradise,' Mrs. Staeheli's rooming house. And when I got near them, she called me and said to me: 'Take this gentleman to the 'Paradise' and tell Mrs. Staeheli that I, the grocer, sent her a guest. He can pay three francs a day and not more than that, and tell her to take him in.' "

"Did Mrs. Staeheli take him in?" Mrs. Sonderegger wanted to know.

"Yes, she took him in. And the stranger asked for a doctor right away, and because Dr. Altherr was just walking by, Mrs. Staeheli called him in. And Dr. Altherr said that the gentleman had fever, and that he would need a lot of rest, good food, and care. And then he asked the stranger if he had not been able to get all those things lately. The stranger did not speak German very well, but he said that was true, he had missed those things for ten years."

"And you were there all the time?" Reinhard asked.

"Yes, and because I took him there, I thought I'd better wait to see if he needed anything else. But he did not need me any longer, because Mrs. Staeheli took care of him herself. She brought the guestbook so he could register, but his hand was so shaky that he could not write at all. So she asked him for his name and he said, Dunant, Henri Dunant. And then Dr. Altherr said that it must be a case of identical names, and then — then I left."

"Did he give you anything?" the children asked.

"Yes, he did," Ferdi answered.

"What?"

"He said he did not have any money. Only three francs a day, from his relatives, and he has to give those to Mrs. Staeheli. But I got something else from him, this beautiful stone." Ferdi took a stone out of his pocket and held it up against the light which was pouring into the room. The stone sparkled and glittered in the sun.

The children all exclaimed noisily and finally their father told them all to go outside. After Mother had put Heini to bed for his nap, she returned to the room with

Father and spoke her thoughts out loud. "Dunant? Do you think that he could be Henri Dunant from Geneva, the one who started the Red Cross?"

"That's impossible," Mr. Sonderegger replied, "he died long ago."

"Maybe prophets don't die," Mother said thoughtfully.

CHAPTER ELEVEN

1908

Heiden's County Hospital had been decorated to celebrate
the day. A triumphal arch of fir branches had been erected
over the entrance, although the hero of the celebration
was not expected to pass through it. He had not passed
through that gate for many years. The County Hospital's
walls housed the poorhouse as well as the hospital itself,
and today all its windows were framed with garlands of
wild flowers. A flag waved from the roof; it was white,
with a red cross in the center.

Old people, paupers, pensioners, and others who lived
in the asylum were sitting on benches in the warm morn-

ing sun. Here, around these sunny walls, they were using up what remained of their lives. In summer, they were all right; but soon, the cold autumn air would force them back into their rooms. The rooms were crowded with metal cots, and there never were enough closets to go around. Today they were glad to be free of those white-walled rooms; free to sit in the soft spring air and talk about the exciting happenings of the day.

"The man from Room Twelve has a birthday." One of the old ladies tried to explain the excitement to the deaf man next to her.

"Who is that?" he asked.

"The man in the single room," she shouted into his ear.

"Did you say he died?"

"It's his birthday. His eightieth."

"Is that so?" The deaf man was satisfied, but not so the old fellow who sat on the woman's other side.

"I am ninety-one," he mumbled. "Ninety-one!" He looked around for recognition. "Nobody ever put out a flag for me."

"Maybe when you get to be a hundred," the old lady giggled.

"He is only eighty, and I am ninety. How is it, then?"

"There's a difference," said his neighbor, rubbing her thumb with her second finger. "Here it is: he is a rich man." She nodded her head as if to emphasize the words. "He has all the money in the world. Sister Emmy told me that he won a hundred thousand francs."

"A hundred thousand francs!" Even the deaf man had understood.

"He did not win that money," said a man who looked out of place among the others. He sat on the far end of the bench.

This man was wearing a decent suit and a gold-rimmed pince-nez; he was younger than the rest. But they all knew that he would never live to be their age, because of his lungs. Now he told his audience that the man from Room Twelve had not won the money but had received a prize, the Nobel Peace Prize, which brought him the respectable sum of one hundred thousand Swiss francs.

"Why did he get it?" asked the woman.

"For his services to the cause of peace," explained the pale man with the pince-nez, "because he was opposed to war."

"For heaven's sake," croaked the ninety-year-old, "who isn't?"

While the paupers on the bench outside quarreled, the man from Room Twelve was being led out of his room by two nephews who had come for this special occasion. Just outside the door, he left the two young men and turned back into his room. Doctor Altherr, Sister Emmy, and the Sister Superior of the house, Sister Elise Bollinger, stood inside the room, waiting for Monsieur to leave them alone so that they could get the room ready for the party.

Monsieur Dunant could not bear to leave his things just lying around. Room Twelve had become his cell during the last sixteen years; as the years wore on, he had left it less and less frequently. Only a few people had visited him there: Doctor Altherr, the two nuns, and until recently, the Sonderegger family. He had stopped seeing them lately because of a difference of opinion with the teacher. No outsiders came into the room except his two nephews, Charles and Maurice, Professor Mueller from Stuttgart, and once, almost thirteen years ago, George Baumberger, a Swiss reporter. In a series of sensational articles, Baumberger disproved the legend of the death of Henri Dunant. He pointed out to his readers the miserable conditions in which lived the once-famous founder of the Red Cross. His reports stirred the public imagination and brought about a change in Dunant's circumstances.

These were the few visitors during the years of solitude, the years Dunant had used to build up his correspondence, to edit his earlier works, to write his memoirs and a history of the Red Cross, hoping always to re-establish himself in respectable society and at last to be appreciated by the world.

On one occasion, he had opened the door of his cell to a woman, an Austrian baroness, Bertha von Suttner. He had a long talk with her, for she shared his spirit of love and his sincere desire for peace. Both of them wanted to eliminate the scourge of mankind, war; and if another book compared in influence with *Souvenir of Solferino*, it was Bertha von Suttner's *Down The Arms*.

No one else had been admitted, although there had been other callers since Dunant was once again recognized by the world. Even Madame Severine, a well-known journalist, had come all the way from Paris without winning admission. She had been permitted a few words with the "hermit of Heiden" on the outside of the glass window in the door of Room Twelve. She could report nothing to her readers except that Dunant's voice seemed unusually thin and high pitched, but it gained in volume and warmth when he began to speak of his work, and that he had said, "I would not receive the King of England if he should come to see me!"

It was not easy, therefore, for Dunant to leave his room to these other people. He pleaded, in an almost childish voice:

"Please, I'll only leave if no one touches anything in my room. Please, Doctor Altherr, see that nobody moves my writings."

He glanced again around the small room which was his study, his bedroom, his entire home. His desk was piled high with manuscripts, notes, outlines and corrected pages. Stacks of newspapers were heaped on his two chairs. Boxes filled with citations and medals, with their descriptive papers, stood on the simple cabinet. What if they lost something, or changed things around? He would have to search for them tomorrow and lose much time doing so. There was so much to do and so little time in which to do it.

When Charles came back into the room and said, "Come, Uncle, nobody will even look at anything," Dunant freed himself from the gentle grip and walked over to the cabinet. Opening the top drawer, he pulled out the scroll granting him the Nobel Peace Prize of the year 1901. He took the document with him, as he would have liked to take everything in the room, and forced himself to leave with his nephews. He felt that he could not spoil his friends' pleasure in the party.

When they reached the steps of the house, the two men turned around to show Monsieur Dunant how everything had been decorated for his birthday. The old gentleman admired the flowers and the garlands, then looked up and murmured to himself,

"The flag!"

He had seen it so often, again and again, in the various cities of Europe. This was the cross he had drawn on the white cloth with his own hands. It would stay here, long after he was gone, to tell the world of his work for peace.

As Monsieur Dunant stood on the top of the stairs, he was noticed by the passers-by. People on the street stopped to wave to him; a few little girls ran over to kiss his hands. Everyone in Heiden recognized the old gentleman with the white beard; only the paupers on their benches did not know him. They stared. Their glances asked what a rich man like this old gentleman could know about life, which meant misery and poverty, hunger and hard work. What does he know about us? they wondered.

The ninety-one-year-old scratched his chin and grinned.

"He looks older than I do."

They all giggled, all except the pale man on the other end of the bench. He blushed; he felt embarrassed, for he realized what Monsieur Dunant had accomplished.

When Monsieur looked at the group of men on the

benches, one after another of them looked away: they
could not meet his eyes. He slept under the same roof;
he ate the same food; he was as old and feeble as most of
them — but he was different. They did not know why.

"He's got money," the old woman explained, after Monsieur Dunant had gone back into the cool, dim hall. "That's
why he is different."

The two young men led their uncle up the stairs, very
slowly. They noticed that he had become excited. Once
in his own corridor, he dropped their arms and walked on
ahead of them. When he reached Room Twelve, Monsieur
Dunant rapped on the door, and it was opened by unseen
hands. The room seemed empty, for everyone had stepped
behind the open door.

Henri Dunant stood alone in the bright, sunny room.
After a short glance around, to make sure that nothing had
been moved, his eyes rested on the pile of presents.

A low, square table had been carried into the room. It
was covered with a white linen cloth. On it was a crystal
bowl, filled with more red roses than anyone had ever seen
gathered in one place. There were other packages on the
floor, and on a hassock, but only the bowl stood on the
table. The old gentleman noticed nothing but the flowers.

Slowly he walked toward the table. Big tears ran freely
down his cheeks. As he walked the few steps to the center
of the room, he seemed to travel the distance back to his
childhood. The fragrance of roses touched his heart and
made him dizzy, and he reached both hands out into the

flowers. Quickly he drew them back, and turning around, tears on his smiling face, showed his pricked hands.

"They still carry thorns, the roses."

Doctor Altherr had to get busy. He pulled out several thorns while his patient sat back in the easy chair. After the little operation was over, Monsieur called his two nephews and pressed their hands. He looked into their eyes, as dark as his own and as dark as his father's.

"I know how many there are, Charles, Maurice," he said cheerfully. "I don't have to count them to know. Who told you of the family custom of adding one rose every year?"

"Father," they answered, and Charles continued: "Father once told us that grandmother used to put a crystal vase on every birthday table, filled with as many red roses as the child had years."

"One more every year," said the old man, "up to eighty. Right? But no more after that!"

"It will be still more beautiful when there are a hundred roses on your table," said Sister Emmy. "Now you should look at the other things."

There was a white flannel robe, its right sleeve decorated with a red cross, from a women's league in Sweden. Doctor Altherr had brought books, including a book by Tolstoy which Monsieur Dunant would have liked to start reading immediately. Sister Emmy had made a pair of slippers, and Monsieur was made to try them on at once. From the Sister Superior came a new black velvet cap made by herself, and when that was tried on, it proved to be too big. Monsieur tried to console Sister by telling her that he would grow into it.

A whole basket of mail waited. It was full of letters and cards, packages and telegrams. On top, left there on purpose, were a few envelopes that bore a royal coat-of-arms or some other distinguished seal. Someone pushed the basket close to the easy chair, and Monsieur Dunant reached for the nearest letter.

"My paper knife, please," he demanded.

Charles interrupted. "Just one moment — "

Maurice had loosened the cork in one of the two bottles of champagne which were cooling in a bucket of ice, and now it popped out all the way to the ceiling.

"Who fired a shot?" Monsieur had turned around, pretending indignation. When he saw the sparkling wine, he laughed. He had recognized the sound although he had not heard it for forty years, but he liked to tease his guests.

Sister Emmy passed the glasses around, and Monsieur joked: "I don't know whether I am allowed to drink this. What do you say, Doctor?"

"If you don't make a habit of asking for champagne for breakfast," the doctor smiled.

"That depends on how I like it. I can't remember what it tastes like."

The guests raised their glasses, and everyone stepped up to Monsieur Dunant, expressing their good wishes. When the Sister Superior smiled her greeting to the old gentleman, he asked:

"Well, Sister, how much longer will you take care of me?"

"Until my own eightieth birthday, I suppose."

"No longer?"

"No, my niece will take over then, until she, too, is eighty."

Then Doctor Altherr addressed the party. "We ought to have a toast now," he said. "Let us raise our glasses to the founder of the Red Cross, Monsieur Henri Dunant, and let us drink to his work, that it may continue to be a blessing to mankind whenever a new war has to be faced."

The cheers were interrupted by Monsieur Dunant, whose voice sounded like a cry. His body shook, and his words resounded in the sudden silence.

"No! I will not drink to that! Do you think it was my idea to make of the Red Cross a fire brigade which would sit and wait for new fires to break out? It is my hope that there shall be no more fires, that the Red Cross shall someday become superfluous, unnecessary except in times of disaster and natural catastrophes. Do you hear me? The Red Cross was founded to mitigate the horrors of war, not to excuse them or make them acceptable."

The old gentleman had talked himself into a state of excitement. It was obvious to his guests that he was no longer talking to them; that the walls of his room had fallen; the borders of countries been abolished; that Dunant spoke to the whole world. The doctor put down his glass and stepped over to his elderly patient.

"Don't worry, Doctor," said Monsieur Dunant. "You may take up your glass again. We have not yet had our toast. Let us drink to the promise that the Red Cross of war may be turned into a Red Cross of peace." He raised the glass to his lips, then set it down suddenly.

"I tell you," Monsieur Dunant went on, "no other war will break out." His voice had lost its sharpness; it was mellow and pleasant. "No other war will break out, because no war has ever broken out! Wars are not diseases breaking forth in the body of mankind like scarlet fever or measles; they are not natural catastrophes, like volcanoes and floods. Every single war in the long, bloody chain which links together the centuries of our history has been *started*.

"Every war has been started by a few individuals, by a handful of fanatics, gamblers or cowards." He turned from one to another of his guests, his eyes pleading his sincerity. "There is one good thing about this, and that is that it is no secret, and it is not inevitable. Those few fanatics are weak and helpless so long as not one of us, not one single one of us, agrees to their murderous plans by active cooperation or by passive hopelessness."

Dunant's hands were raised, his eyes shone. The five people who listened to him felt as if one of the sages had returned to them. His words, however, were down-to-earth, calling each person present to his responsibilities.

"What we need," he went on, "are men without fear and without hatred, full of hope, be it even hope against hope. Only when the world is at its most hopeless, when everyone expects war, will the huge roulette wheel come to a stop and the ball roll into that fatal slot — war!"

This vision of renewed horror almost overcame the old man. He fell back into his chair. Sister Emmy tried to take the glass from his hand, but he waved her away, and he would not let Doctor Altherr take his pulse. His voice was quiet now, and childlike, and his words were calm.

"You must help. Everybody must help. Let us act with our whole strength, with kindness and love, with the courage of hope, in the cause of peace.

"This is what I ask of you today, on my eightieth birthday. Let us now raise our glasses to drink to that goal."

The guests were profoundly moved. Raising their glasses, they waited until Monsieur was ready to drink, then emptied them to the last drop.

Monsieur Dunant did not look up. Doctor Altherr gave them a sign to withdraw quietly, and the party was over.

The old gentleman fell asleep while Sister Emmy was still pulling down the shades. Hearing him breathe evenly, she tiptoed out.

Henri Dunant, the "Man in White," deserved his rest.

Only two birthdays were left for him to celebrate before he closed his eyes forever on October 30th, 1910.